The Country Wife

Books by DOROTHY VAN DOREN

STRANGERS
FLOWERING QUINCE
BROTHER AND BROTHER
THOSE FIRST AFFECTIONS
DACEY HAMILTON
THE COUNTRY WIFE

WILLIAM SLOANE ASSOCIATES

Publishers   *New York*

The Country Wife

DOROTHY VAN DOREN

Illustrated by Mimi Korach

The chapter "Man, the Maker" originally appeared in
Harper's Bazaar under the title "The Country Wife,"
Copyright 1950 by Hearst Magazines, Inc.

Copyright, 1950, by

DOROTHY VAN DOREN

Typography and format designed by
LEONARD W. BLIZARD

Manufactured in the United States of America
Published simultaneously in Canada by
George J. McLeod, Ltd., Toronto

To M., C., AND J.

By whom I have done less than
justice in these pages

Contents

The Country Wife

1. The Rite of May

EVERY year the business of packing up to go to the country seems to get worse. My husband is a university professor and we spend four long months at our farm in Connecticut. This period is the occasion for jeers and envy on the part of our friends. Pretty nice vacation, they say; not bad at all—four months, one-third of a year, off. There are two catches in this: one, during the eight months he is teaching the Professor works ten hours a day seven days a week; two, he also works very hard three of the four "vacation" months. But since it is in the country, in a study off in a meadow, it doesn't look like work to a toiler in the city.

However, that has nothing to do with packing up. I begin to plan for it, with the help of our devoted household tyrant Martha, early in May: rugs to be cleaned, wrapped in brown paper, and put away; hangings to be taken down and sent to the laundry or the cleaners; dig out the old worn slipcovers and put them on the furniture; stow away small objects. Etcetera.

And decide what to take.

Now this is a curious thing. Years ago, when we bought our house in the country, I decided that we should, as far as possible, equip the farm so that we should not have to cart a load back and forth from the city each spring and fall. Accordingly I bought bedding for the country, table silver for the country, the usual kitchen furnishings, and the like.

When it comes time to pack up for the summer, this laudable effort on my part seems to make no difference whatever.

First there are the books: a new book will be written this summer—the usual routine. That means a small library all to itself. The books must be piled, wrapped, and tied, and stood under the piano to wait for moving day. Then there are always the boys' books, a great variety and number, which they will faithfully arrange in their country bedrooms and never have time to read. I usually take the books I got for Christmas and have not yet read. For some reason they are likely to be both large and heavy.

Then the phonograph records. This is a major problem. It requires about three family conferences to decide which to take, and they are so cumbersome that in the car they have to be treated like a large, limp child with St. Vitus dance. If you are not watching them closely they slip off the seat onto the floor, with disastrous consequences to the next item—my plants.

If I did not have plants I would save myself a great deal of time, labor, anxiety, and tender nursing care. I would also not have to bring the plants down to the city in the

fall and take them back in the spring. But I like plants. I'm
not even ashamed of it. Some of the nicest people like
plants. And I seem to have a modest gift for them. I can
take a poor sickly specimen, fit for nothing but the garbage
can—and if I had any sense I'd put it there—and I
nurse it and turn it around and wash off the leaves and
admire it judiciously, and first thing you know it is growing like a house afire.

A plant is not like a book, which presents a flat, box-like
surface to be wrapped and tied. Not at all. Plants stick
up and stick out and—be careful! You'll knock off that
begonia flower and I had a time getting it to bloom . . .
You put them in a carton. All right, you put them in two or
three cartons. Naturally, the cartons have to stand on the
floor of the car, in the back, and nothing can be piled on
top of it—I mean them. (One of my plants presents a
problem that I have not told anybody about yet. It is a
cactus, not supposed to grow much, but nobody ever told
the poor thing that; so it has grown and grown, not any
place but up, a long, straight, not-too-steady spike which
I have not measured because I'd rather not know how long
it is. It is certainly going to cause trouble when we pack
up.)

Books and records and plants. . . . We have always
taken two typewriters, the Professor's portable and my
old L. C. Smith; but now that the boys are grown, they
also like a typewriter apiece, one of them being a large,
outsize affair that my older son bought at a bargain from
Air Force Supply. Four typewriters, therefore, and one
typewriter table, metal, rigid, non-collapsible.

Then the boxes from the kitchen. We have known all

winter that we should leave town for the summer, come the end of May. You would think there would be no perishable food to carry. But it never works out that way. There are always a couple of loaves of bread and a half-bottle of milk—well, you can't throw away good food, not when so many people are hungry and it costs so much—and the remains of Sunday's roast, and the olive oil we can't buy in a little New England town, and half a chocolate cake. Things like that. Not to mention the electric mixer; we can't be expected to have two electric mixers. And the electric iron, because the country iron is on its last legs. And those new wine glasses I bought at the sale. About three cartons will perhaps hold all this and they can go in the luggage compartment.

Then there are at least four suitcases—maybe one or two more—and four fat briefcases. And the boys' top-coats; these couldn't possibly fit into the suitcases. Just throw them on top. And the tennis racquets and the violin and the clarinet—and, oh yes, the pile of music. And I want to take that lamp up; we don't need it in town and it will be fine for the upstairs study.

I really think that is all.

Every year it is the same. My husband, a miraculously resourceful packer, patiently lines up all the stuff in the hall and surveys it with an expert's eye. Nobody gives him advice when he packs the car. Nobody even hands him things. Once in a while he mumbles to himself, but I do not listen. Much better not listen; no telling what you would hear. The packing takes a long time. I say at last: "I can take those records up on the seat between us." He gives me a look and goes on tying them in piles and wedging them between suitcases on the back seat. "I'm sorry there seem to be so many big plants," I say nervously. No answer, not even a look this time. Maybe he didn't hear. Just as well.

Of course there isn't room for the boys, but mercifully they have gone off to visit friends and are coming up on the train next week. Martha will stay in town to do last-minute chores about closing the house. It might have been better if I had planned to come on the train, too, I think wistfully—but at least I can help unload when we arrive. There are no restrictions on unloading; any fool with a strong back can do it. It takes a genius to pack.

Eventually it is done. The back seat of the car is piled to the roof, the trunk is full to the last square inch. God preserve us from a flat tire! If we had to get out the spare from underneath that pile of gear in the back, I would shoot myself. I take my coat and my husband's coat and throw them over the seat between us. I put my handbag in the glove compartment—no, it won't fit; put it on the seat, with the two Hershey bars and the cigarettes. My husband gets in and sits behind the wheel.

We are off. Everything is under control, except that it begins to rain hard. So we start off in the rain. It is May, but the city looks grimy and gray. The pavements are black with rain, trucks roaring by splash our newly washed windows; there is a lot of traffic on the highway. The first part of the trip is slow, the windshield wiper does not work too well, the asphalt is slippery when wet. It is a dismal ride. Maybe, I muse, it's all a mistake. Maybe we ought to stay in town and take a two-weeks' trip as so many others do. Maybe the house in the country is a foolish luxury, profligate of energy as well as money. We are not as young as we once were. It looks as though it would never stop raining. Why do we always have to start out in the rain?

The suitcases are slipping a little. We go around a curve and they come perilously near pitching down on top of the best begonia. I put my arm back to steady them. "Knew I should have tied them," the Professor mutters to himself. "It's nothing," I say brightly, "I can easily hold them steady." "I'll tie them," he says.

We stop on the side of the highway, in the rain, and he gets out, opens the trunk, pulls out an extra piece of heavy twine—how did he know he would need it?—closes the trunk, opens the car door, takes out the largest box of plants so as to have some place to stand in the car, and winds the twine tightly around the suitcases, fastening the end firmly to the door handle. It is an awkward job and there is not room to do it easily. The carton of plants stands in the rain, all right for the plants but not too good for the carton.

"This box is wet. Does that matter?" he asks, putting the dripping carton back into the car.

"Not a bit," I say, still cheery. (But be careful when you take them out, I warn myself; they're likely to go all of a heap, when next disturbed.)

The suitcases are now as steady as a rock. The type-writer table, however, wedged on its side above the piles of books, has moved slightly and one of the legs is threatening to pierce my ear to the brain. I do not remark on it. I move my head at a forty-five degree angle and pretend to be taking a nap. "Sleepy?" asks the Professor. "Want a bite of chocolate? I do, anyhow." With my head still on one side like an inquisitive puppy, I unwrap the first Hershey bar and give him a piece. Wonder if almond milk chocolate is good for a serious brain injury. I'll try it.

As I munch, holding my head carefully to avoid the typewriter table leg, I am reminded of last fall, when we started back to town with the same sort of load. We have a small, ancient truck that serves us as an extra car—the boys can drive themselves to the lake, for example, and I still have the car to go marketing. The truck had to be left at the garage to be put in dead storage for the winter. My husband said: "You drive the car, I'll take the truck, and I'll meet you at the garage. Remember, the brakes grab a little."

I hate to drive the truck; it has a way of going dead when you stop at a crossroad and refusing to start again. So I got into the car willingly enough, adjusted my skirt, turned the ignition key, and put my foot on the starter. With the utmost care I started off—I knew very well the brakes grabbed; they also bucked like a cowboy on an untamed broncho. I would certainly be careful. I moved my foot to the accelerator and released the hand-brake. The car started gently downhill. I do not know what happened next, or why it happened. But I put my foot hastily on the foot-brake; the brakes grabbed, the car stopped with a resounding jerk, and five suitcases hurtled forward from the back seat, draping themselves around my neck and dropping on top of my precious plants on the floor. With dignity I extricated myself. "Take your car," I said succinctly. "I'll drive the truck if it kills me."

That had been last fall. Nothing like that will happen today. In the first place, the brakes have been fixed. Also I am not driving. Also the suitcases are tied. The only thing likely to happen now is that my ear may be gored by the table leg. But I'll fool it. I'll keep my eyes straight in front. If it hits me now I'll probably have a concussion, but I'll have all summer to get over it.

We went around another curve. "Ouch!" I said in a loud voice.

My husband looked at me hastily. "What's wrong?"

"Oh, nothing," I said, rubbing the back of my neck. "I may be getting a little headache."

"Too bad," he said, sympathetically. "Lean back and close your eyes."

If I leaned back the table leg would go right through my head. Closing my eyes would not help one way or the other. "It isn't bad," I said. There must have been something odd in my voice, for this time my husband really looked at me.

He brought the car to a stop on the shoulder of the road. "Why didn't you tell me?" he said.

As he had done before, he got out of the car, opened the trunk, took out another piece of twine—wonderful man!—closed the trunk, opened the car door, and unwedged the typewriter table, raking the side of my face and removing my hat as he did so.

"Sorry," he said.

"Not at all," I replied politely.

"Should have tied this. Everything ought to be tied. Remember that next time."

"Were you telling me?" I asked, startled.

He looked equally startled, then smiled. "Just talking to myself," he said.

It was still raining.

We broke out the other Hershey bar and he smoked several cigarettes. I dislike smoking in cars unless the windows are open, and if I opened my window a cascade of water poured down my shoulder. With the blessed relief of no longer being teased by a steel spear, I leaned back and closed my eyes. I suppose I slept a little. When I woke we were stopping at a garage. "Gas?" I asked.

"Flat tire," said my husband in the voice of Napoleon describing the battle of Waterloo.

"God help us," I said in a hushed voice. My husband also made some reference to God. I stammered: "Are you going to open the trunk?"

No answer. A man came running out with a raincoat over his head. "Can I drive in somewhere?" my husband asked. Directed by the garage man standing on the running board, we drove into a small, cluttered garage. My husband spoke distinctly, through his teeth. "I want a new tire and tube."

"No spare?" asked the garage man rashly.

"We have a spare, yes; we always have a spare. At the moment it might just as well be in China as where it is. A new tire and tube, please."

"Right," said the garage man, and began operations with his jack.

I got out and flattened myself against the wall of the garage. The rain was descending in sheets. Ho hum. A jolly life in the country. I had been longing to see the new daffodils we had planted with such hopeful energy last fall. At the thought of the bedraggled rags they would be now, I averted my face. The lawn would be a foot high. The crab apple blossoms—our crab apple tree has a trunk two feet through and when it is in bloom it looks like a huge white umbrella—would never get fertilized. No self-respecting bee would fly in such weather. What fun to be a self-respecting bee and sit snugly dry in the hive, eating honey and new wax while it rained. Personally I hate honey, but I am not, of course, a bee.

The jack unwound, the car sank slowly down on its fat, new tire. The old tire was standing disconsolately against the wall. "Pretty good tire," said the garage man. "Fix it for you? Won't take long."

My husband looked at our load. There was not room for an insect—that old bee that would not fly out of the hive in the rain, for instance—on top of what we already had.

"I could take it on my lap," I giggled. Might as well inject a note of cheer.

"Keep it," said my husband. "Give it to the starving Armenians, hang it on the Christmas tree, cut it up for rubber bands."

"I know how you feel," said the garage man, with a we-men-understand-each-other air, as if the entire load were my idea. "O.K., I'll give you a dollar for it."

"Much obliged," said my husband, and began to back out of the garage in the rain.

"Was that the bad tire?" I asked, unwisely.

"No, it was the best. The bad one is on the right rear."

I sighed. Maybe we would have another flat tire. Maybe we would have three more flat tires. In that case the cost of the trip would come to eighty dollars or so. We bought the best tires. Hm. *Hm!*

But we did not have any more tire trouble. We merely had rain. The countryside through which we were now passing, having left the highways behind, was drenched, soaked, drowned. Daffodils that some silly woman had planted last fall were flat in the mud. Fruit blossoms were transparent and limp on the branches. Lilac bushes were bent double with the weight of dripping flower heads. Who invented the country anyway? Who thought up summer vacations? Maybe the trouble was who thought up automobiles? Without a car, we would not be able to take all this stuff; we'd get at the spare tire easily (there seemed to be something wrong with that reasoning, but I did not bother to find out what it was). We should have to write with a pen and make our own music on the piano, and read the books that were already at the farm, and I would not have those foolish plants. At that thought I became so miserable that I resolved to go to sleep again. The chocolate was all gone and there was no scenery worth staying awake for.

I woke, with the homing pigeon's instinct for the

roost, just as the car turned into our lane. My husband had opened his window wide and a fresh breeze blew across my face. "It's stopped raining," I cried.

"Uh-huh. Stopped half an hour ago. I don't think it's rained much here. Road doesn't look bad."

It was true. The grass track in the center of the dirt road was standing up pert and green. The fields on either side were green, too, with hay in which a few daisies had already bloomed out. The air was heavy with the scent of apple trees in full flower, and the bees were working overtime. As we stopped before our own gate, I could see that the whole side yard was edged with daffodils, none broken, none mashed, none soaked. I jumped out of the car and ran into the yard. The smells were so wonderfully familiar, a mixture of damp new grass, lilacs, and fresh manure just spread on the garden. A beautiful country smell, the prelude to four months away from town. My husband was standing at the gate with his nose in the air. He grinned at me. "Smells good, doesn't it?" he said.

I nodded. In a few minutes we should have to begin the backbreaking job of unloading the car, and I would have to put things away, unpack the bags, light the kitchen fire, and start to get supper. Next fall we would pack the same sort of load and tote it wearily back to town. None of this mattered in the least. For the moment, I was simply smelling.

2. Man, the Maker

O N evenings in late June we never eat supper until nine o'clock. This is partly because Martha is on vacation, and we can eat when we please. And partly because this is the only part of the summer when the Professor really stops reading or writing—it is his real vacation, in other words—and works as the carpenter God probably intended him to be. He loves carpentry. He can turn out a neat cocktail table, a solid bench, or a set of drawers that would entitle him to a union card any day. There is only one thing about his carpentry: When he starts something, he will not stop until it is finished. He . . . will . . . not . . . stop!

He begins early in the morning, reluctantly and quickly gobbles the lunch I take out to the table in the yard, and begs for a late supper. It doesn't matter to me. I like the long evenings too, and the boys don't object as long as they can stuff themselves with bologna sandwiches at the usual supper hour.

It should be understood, however, that because the

Professor is working in the shop, it does not mean he dislikes company. From time to time each of us comes to the door to admire his handiwork. The boys poke in the box of old iron for suitable latches or hinges. I mix the stain I shall use when the object has been made. Staining is always my job, and I have developed quite a knack for it. When he works in the shop, family life is friendly and pleasant.

It is different when he works in the house.

We have very few hot days in June in our part of Connecticut, but let Father begin to build a set of shelves in one of the upstairs rooms under the eaves, and the temperature rises promptly to eighty-five in the shade and does not budge till sundown. Under the eaves, of course, it is much hotter. I say: "Look, it's awfully warm up here. Why don't you wait for a rainy day?"

"You want these shelves, don't you?" he asks sternly.

"Of course I want them. But I don't want them enough for you to die of sunstroke while you're making them."

"I don't mind the heat. I've told you that." It is true. He has told me many times. It is only effete Easterners who complain of the heat. A Middle-Westerner like himself is accustomed to long, hot days and long, hot, corn-growing nights. I decide to make iced tea. That will help.

The sound of sawing goes on upstairs; a long, wrenching, gritty sound, with plenty of perspiration behind it; now and then there is the plop of a board to the floor. I hear steps overhead. He is coming downstairs, leaving a trail of golden sawdust wherever he walks.

"You may not mind heat," I tell him, "but your face is red as the side of the barn. Here's a cool drink."

"In a minute," he says absent-mindedly, as he goes out to the toolhouse for another board. When he comes back he reaches for the tall, beaded glass in which ice tinkles prettily, without stopping his walk.

"You're not going to take that drink upstairs?" I ask plaintively.

"Sure, why not? Got to keep on with this. You don't want the house upset too long."

I sigh. I go out into the yard and sternly, with my ears closed to sounds of sawing, kneel down to weed the edge of the perennial border. It is hot in the sun but I like it. I already have my first layer of tan, and can admire my browning knees while dragging out a stubborn clump of *Portulaca oleracea*, or pussley to its many non-friends. There is a particularly long, agonized screech from the saw that I cannot fail to hear, and my husband appears at the window of our bedroom, where he is working. "Come up for a minute?" he invites, in a voice which carries overtones of doom.

I drop the pussley and my trowel and run for the house. It is better, I have learned, to run in answer to this sort of summons. The roof may have started to cave in and my shoulder may be needed to hold it up.

I run up the winding stair covered with sawdust, and along the hall to our bedroom (more sawdust). Our furniture has been moved into the center of the floor. The bed is piled with objects from the bureau (my best bottle of toilet water is lying on its side, but with a prayer for the security of the cap, I decide this is no time to retrieve it), not to mention the rocking chair turned upside down on a pile of clean wash (I knew I should have put that away).

In the corner where the shelves will be are a stack of sweet-smelling pine boards, the sawhorse, the saw, the sawer, and plenty of sawdust. There is, in fact, sawdust everywhere.

"Want a hand?" I ask.

"Hold this," says my husband grimly. I put my knee on the long board balanced on the sawhorse. It slips and flops with a horrible clatter to the floor. Patiently he picks it up, ignoring my apologies. "Not your knee," he says. "Just hold the end with your hands to steady it. I'll do the knee work."

So I move to the end of the board, straddle it, and grasp it firmly with both hands. My head is bent under the low ceiling of the eaves and my rear end is firmly wedged against the closet door, in which the edge of the board is digging long deep ridges. Nevertheless I hold steady. That is what the carpenter has ordered me to do, and I shall do it if it ruins me and the woodwork at the same time. The temperature in the room must be 120. The Professor, clad in blue overalls and a blue chambray shirt, the country costume he loves best, is soaked with sweat. My shirt is sticking to my back and my nose itches. Nevertheless, I cling to my board for dear life. With his knee firm against the board, my husband begins to saw. It is, I tell myself, much harder for him than for you. Sawing is hard work, particularly for New York muscles used to doing little more than hanging to a subway strap. He looks tired out already. Wish he'd stop. The silliest wish of the year, so far.

At last the board is sawed through, the short end drops to the floor, the long end, which I am holding, slides

against the inside of my leg just where my shorts end, removing about an inch and a half of skin and leaving splinters. Pine boards are rougher than they used to be.

"All right?" I ask, hiding my suffering.

"Thanks very much. I may call you again. Can't seem to manage these long boards in this little space."

I retire to put iodine on my skinned flesh, after extracting six splinters, two of which break off. If we hired a carpenter, it would cost a lot. And the shelves will be wonderful to have. The fact that we have done without them for fifteen or twenty years doesn't mean they aren't needed.

I go out to the yard again and resume my weeding, but in a shady spot. No sense in both of us dying with sunstroke. The ground is in beautiful condition, damp, loamy, friable. No wonder the weeds like it. The clumps of delphinium are about to bloom. There were four white lilies out this morning, and the red poppies are as big as dinner plates. I love the country. I wouldn't give up this house for anything—even though we must build shelves on a hot day.

I am lost in a deep dream of country peace when there comes a loud sound from the house like a mad bull being deprived of his favorite china shop. Sore leg and all, I run!

"What?" I gasp, as I make the top of the stairs in two jumps and the length of the hall in a slide.

My husband's language would never be approved by the American Association of University Professors and it had better not be recorded here. But the board he has just sawed is too short.

"Oh," I say weakly, sitting on the nearest chair, with its coating of sawdust, "I thought you had cut your arm off or something."

He glares. That was not a tactful thing to say, and I know it, too late. He grits his teeth. He is about to speak again and controls himself with obvious effort. But he gives the offending board a sharp kick and sends it flying against the sawhorse, which topples over, scoring the wall and upsetting the box of nails.

Perhaps the kick got the exasperation out of his system. At least he looks at me with an embarrassed grin and picks up another board. "Want to hold?" he says.

I hold. This time I protect my leg when the board slides, but at the expense of my left wrist—three splinters and a skinned patch about two inches square. They really should do something about these boards. Maybe I could get a job in a planing mill. It would be worth it in the long run—a way to save my skin, so to speak.

His thanks this time are quite profuse. I go downstairs

to think about lunch. There is a rattley bang which means the boys and the truck have come back from the lake. It is too hot to eat in the yard, so I set the pitcher of milk on the table, and the big bowl of salad—we are cutting our own lettuce now and those are our radishes—with cold lamb for them to make their own sandwiches. For a special treat there is a bowl of strawberries bought at a high price from the local store. It surprises me afresh each summer to find that food in the country costs more than in New York.

I go to the foot of the stairs. "Lunch!" I say hopefully. "Come now. You're ready for a breathing spell."

Maybe it is because he kicked the board, or maybe even he is ready to quit for a while. At any rate, to my amazement, he comes, stopping to wash up on the way. We sit down peacefully in the cool dining room—relatively cool, that is—and make our meal. From swimming and tennis, the boys are already a fine dark tan. They look hearteningly healthy. The cream for the strawberries is so thick it needs to be spooned out. The lettuce is green and fresh and tender. Out in the sunny yard the ramblers are beginning to bloom.

My younger son leans back in his chair and stretches his long legs under the table. "Good lunch," he says of my modest efforts. "Bet it's hot in town!"

My heart melts at such a thought. I wish that everybody could be in the country, lunching on strawberries and cream, out of the hot sun. I am grateful that I am a professor's wife. I am especially grateful to have married a professor who is at heart a carpenter. You get such nice shelves.

"Is the sawing all done?" I ask.

"Just about. Except for the molding."

"You can bite that off with your teeth," our elder son remarks facetiously.

His father bends an eyebrow at him. "Did you happen to buy any more sixpenny nails, after you used up the old ones?" he inquires hopefully.

"Gosh, Dad, I didn't. I'll hop in the truck and get you some. Be back in a trice, whatever that is."

The Professor leans back and shakes his head, more in sorrow than in anger. "Of course you didn't. Of course you'll just hop in the truck. You'll drive twelve miles to get a couple of pounds of nails, when you were within twenty feet of the hardware store yesterday—and probably the day before."

Our son is penitent but not crushed. He taps his father's head with a long brown finger as he walks around the table. "Father, I will buy you a gallon of gas," he says. "Maybe two gallons. See you!" He breaks into a long lope as the screen door slams behind him, and we hear the truck engine protesting as he bumps down the hill.

"Will you have to wait till he gets back?" I ask.

"Oh, no. I've got enough nails to start. Maybe enough for the whole job. I just wanted to impress that boy with his forgetfulness."

"Hm," I say, and catch a look from our younger boy which says plainly: I'll remember that! The Professor rises, stretches, and walks out into the yard to the toolhouse, bringing back presently a couple of twelve-foot lengths of molding which are exceedingly difficult to maneuver into the door, around the hall, through the living room, and up the narrow stairs. He makes several comments on the way that would do nothing to further his advancement at the University if they were overheard by the Board of Trustees. Or maybe they would; you can't even tell about trustees these days. Everything is changing.

I wash the dishes. The older boy comes back with the nails and departs, with his brother, to the lake to play tennis. "We'll do the lawn this evening," they tell me cheerfully, as they jump into the truck once more.

"You'd better," I retort, "unless you want to scythe it first."

The hot afternoon wears on. The bees are loud in the meadow back of the house, thick with purple clover. I lie on my chaise longue on the lawn and wonder if I should read a book. I take a nap instead. Sawing has ceased upstairs. There is only hammering now, steady hammering. Those shelves will be done in no time! Better make some more iced tea.

Just before I am ready to carry it upstairs the telephone rings. It is my sister, five miles away. "Come on over to the lake for a swim," she says, "and all of you drive back here for a drink and picnic." It is a lovely idea. The boys would like it; I would myself. But there are the shelves. "I'm afraid not," I say sadly. "We're building shelves."

"Oh," she says understandingly. The Professor's carpentry and his methods of work are famous in the family. "Make it tomorrow. He'll be done by then, won't he?"

"Oh, yes," I say joyfully. If there is one thing I am sure of, it is that the shelves will be done before tomorrow.

Yet even with the prospect of tomorrow, I am a little depressed as I mount the sawdust-covered stairs with the pitcher of iced tea and two glasses. Childishly, I should like to have gone today.

It is still dripping hot upstairs. This is an unusual day; a hot, sticky, irritating day. It is a day for the absolute minimum of exertion. I regard the bedroom, yellow with sawdust, the disarranged furniture, the ends of pine boards everywhere, the nails strewn about the floor. It will take me half the night to get it in order so that we can go to bed. I didn't need the shelves that much. Probably I didn't need them at all.

I do not say this. I do not really mean it. But it is so hot!

My husband wipes his sleeve across his forehead and smiles at me as he takes his cold drink. "Wonderful!" he says. "Just what I wanted. Now you're here, you might steady a board or two. Get done faster. Who was that called?"

"It was Sister," I say, and try not to be bitter as I add, "she wanted us to come over for a picnic supper."

"Hm," he replies. "Nice idea." But I get the impression that he has not really heard me.

It is half-past three, the hottest part of the day. But until almost six, I steady boards, collect nails, offer iced tea (for which I have gone down to fetch more ice), and in general provide moral support while the Professor hammers. My face is as red as his by now. I am afraid of losing a finger or thumb under the hammer. There is sawdust down my neck, and on my bare legs and arms, and wherever it touches me, it sticks. I think of floating in the cool lake (it is much too hot to swim), or of taking a bath (probably in some special solution which will dissolve the resin with which I am varnished), and then of put-

ting on a fresh chambray dress and clean white sneakers
and lying on the grass under Sister's oak tree with something in a tall glass in my hand—not iced tea. This, of
course, is the most idle daydreaming. Under the eaves it is
still hot as an oven. The boys have long since called up and
announced they were going to their aunt's for a picnic:
Sorry you can't come, Mother—how are the shelves?

I don't care how the shelves are. I am sick and tired of
the shelves. I wish shelves had not been invented. Much
better to put books on the floor; or for that matter, who
wants books? We've got thousands of books and hundreds
of shelves and—how in Heaven's name did sawdust get
inside my shirt around my waist?

At five fifty-five my husband straightens his back and
wipes his forehead on his sleeve for the last time. "There!"
he says proudly. "Got it done sooner than I expected. You
want to stain it today?"

"Not today," I say very gently. "No, I think not today."
He does not argue, although I know he disapproves. A job
ought to be finished by nightfall—that is his creed. But it
is not mine. He picks up the board ends, the tools, the
nails. I get out the vacuum cleaner and sweep the bedroom
and the hall and stairs and all the way out to the side door.
We put the furniture to rights. It is nearly seven-thirty.
We are both utterly exhausted, but only I am willing to
admit it. I should like to make a speech about it in Madi-
son Square Garden—if I could find the breath!

It is cooler outdoors, and as I walk wearily from the
toolhouse to hang up the pail I have just emptied of sawdust, I notice that it is getting dark. "What time is it?" I
ask. The sun doesn't set till eight o'clock or so.

Just then I hear a sound and my husband hears it, too. We turn in the yard and face each other, amazement and delight on our faces. It was unmistakably a clap of thunder! A cool breeze has sprung up like a miraculous gift from nowhere. A big drop falls on my nose. And after that, the deluge! We ought to run for the house. It is a real thunderstorm, with great forks of lightning and mountainous booms of thunder. But instead, we stand out in the yard and lift our faces to the cool rain. It pelts our eyes and soaks our hair; it washes us clean of sawdust and perspiration and fatigue and petty irritation—my petty irritation, not his. We are clean and fresh. We are actually cold!

"Isn't it wonderful," I shout above the loudest thunderclap of all. "I'm so glad you built the shelves! Let's go in and change now and have supper by the fire—I'm freezing!"

The Professor nods and laughs and this time we both run, hand in hand, to the house, out of the storm.

3. The Cold and Glorious Fourth

THE Fourth of July in our family begins early in the morning. My husband is not an early riser. When I am feeling cross and persecuted, one of the things I say with grim humor is that if I did not get up in the morning nobody else in the family ever would. Not ever. But on July 4 it is different. Shortly after dawn the bed next to mine is empty. Shortly after that the innocent new day is split from top to bottom by a fearful bang (cannon cracker No. 1, followed immediately by cannon crackers No. 2, 3, 4, etc.). I wake. Who wouldn't? Jolly voices are calling me from the yard below. I arise grumpily and go to the window. It is, of course, my husband and his two friends—the Three Professors.

"Did you hear that?" they shout, dancing around in the grass, which is probably very wet at that hour.

I forebear to make the stock answers like "Do you think I have totally lost my hearing!" They look quite funny, and instead of answering them I laugh. I can't help it.

That was the way the day began. That was the way

the Fourth always began. Many years before it had become established that Alfred, an outwardly sedate professor of philosophy, and his wife and son, and Joe, a less sedate and rather jumpy logician, with his wife—no son yet—should spend the Fourth of July with us in Connecticut. We three wives got along very well; the children were fast friends, and the Three Professors at our house on July 4 were just boys together, no two ways about it. Just boys together, making noise on Independence Day.

So the day began with a bang. The three little boys, ranging in age from four to ten, were by now out of bed and planning to dash downstairs in their pajamas. But it was much too cold. "Come back and get dressed," I told them sternly, "and don't forget your sweaters." Sweaters and all, it didn't take them much more than three minutes to get down to the yard.

The dogs had disappeared. Even as I began to dress, I heard a scrabbling on the stairs, and our fat old black chow (well, part chow, anyway) galloped through the hall like a wild young thing and settled himself under my bed. He would stay there, poor creature, until the celebration ended. The Newfoundland, Shonko, who was slightly larger than a bull calf, and the police dog, Sam, and Pup, the pup, had set out a minute or two earlier in a strong lope for the opposite side of the Hollow, two miles away, where they could retire in peace and quiet to our neighbor's tall pines. Their pace was much too fast for the old chow, and rather fast for Pup, just an ordinary mixed breed with short legs, and a midget compared to the other two. However, what Pup lacked in breeding he made up in brains, for when the big dogs went too fast for him he would hang onto Shonko's plumy tail and catch a ride. After a while the black tail was no longer plumy, but it was just as good for riding.

Mrs. Alfred, Mrs. Joe, and I, having dressed in a leisurely manner, went downstairs and sat by the remains of last night's fire while the explosions outdoors continued. By breakfast time, a good many of the cannon crackers were gone.

"Aren't you nearly out of giants?" I said hopefully.

"Almost," my husband replied with a sad look. But at this point Joe's eyes lighted up—he was the logician—and he jumped out of his chair and darted out of the dining room.

"Just a minute, just a minute!" he was saying rapidly as he returned. My husband and Alfred began to beam. Joe rubbed his hands as he laid a large flat package on the breakfast table. "A little surprise, a little surprise—a present for my hostess!" He handed me the package with a bow, I unwrapped it, smiling brightly, and passed it to my husband. Of course it was more cannon crackers.

At this all three of them rubbed their hands, the little boys jumped for joy, the three women smiled resigned smiles, and the tumult and the shouting began all over again.

When lunchtime came around most of the loudest noisemakers had been discharged by varying procedures. Some of the cannon crackers had been put in coffee cans and lighted with a long taper and a fast sprint in the opposite direction. The very largest ones—five-inch, I think they were—were put under a small barrel, which when the firecracker exploded bounced six feet into the

air. Let me say at once that the children were not permitted to take part in these exploits. No, indeed. Even
when they got to be big boys, fourteen or more, it was the
Three Professors who did the fancy shooting—not to
mention most of the plain. The Fourth of July was their
day, and they had practically all the fun.

In the afternoon everybody but me went to the lake to
swim. By then they were hoarding supplies for the "display" fireworks after dark. Which brings me to another
traditional aspect of July 4. Beginning when the boys
were very small, they were permitted on that day to stay
up till the party was over. Nobody even hinted at bed-
time. There was, of course, a practical reason for this—it
was after nine when dark fell, and the modest pile of
rockets and pinwheels had to wait until the light was
gone.

I didn't especially want to swim—it was much too
cold, for one thing; I couldn't remember such a cold
Fourth. And I had various errands in connection with
supper and the refreshments after the night fireworks
had been set off. Also I planned to take a nap!

It was Martha's first year with us and she had invited
a friend to see the fireworks with her. My mother, who
lived down the hill, also had a friend. None of these ladies
was in her first youth, and I fished out a great pile of
steamer rugs and sweaters and blankets to wrap up in
while the show went on. If I had but known it, I should
have got out footwarmers, electric heating pads, and red
flannel underwear. There was a brisk west wind that did
not die down at suppertime. The children came home

from the lake looking blue around the gills. The other wives and the Three Professors had not gone swimming after all, and although they were prepared to give me a dozen good reasons why, I did not need them. "I know," I said. "It was too cold."

"How did you guess?" asked Joe, and having lighted a small firecracker behind me, laughed long and loud when I jumped.

"I thought you were saving them for tonight," I said.

"We are," said my husband firmly. "I am not going to light another one." At that moment there was a loud bang two feet from Mrs. Joe. She also jumped and set her jaw.

"Now, we have got to stop this," said my husband in his most professorial tone. "Alfred, I want you to watch those boys carefully, and Joe, you watch the women. I don't want any more shooting—not till it gets dark." The little boys were rolling around the grass in delight, because even as he spoke there was another bang, and Alfred smiled and took a bow.

We managed to get through supper without much more noise. Then we went down the hill to fetch Grandma and her visitor, and Martha's friend Mabel. We lined up the canvas chairs in a row in the shelter of the house, and put the two ladies in them, well wrapped with blankets around shoulders and knees. Martha and Mabel, however, refused to come out at all. "We can see just as well from the kitchen window," they told me, "and we'll be a whole lot warmer." I could appreciate the truth of this; in fact I envied them. But of course I was obliged to join the sturdy pioneers outside.

I put on a wool suit with a sweater under the jacket. Since this seemed inadequate against the Arctic night, I wound a wool scarf around my head and struggled into a topcoat. The other women were dressed along the same lines, mostly in extra old clothes, more useful than fashionable, that we keep for emergencies. We must have looked like stuffed sausages. We got into the canvas chairs and the men wrapped us, cocoon-like, in blankets. I could just keep from shivering. The boys, however, were galloping around with khaki shorts, bare legs, and one sweater. It is very fine to be young and hot-blooded.

"Don't you think it's dark enough?" I asked through chattering teeth.

"Won't be long now," Alfred said soothingly. "Not cold, are you?"

"C-c-certainly not!" I s-s-said.

As I waited for the display to begin—the professors were busy hammering together a frame to shoot off the rockets—I jammed my hands in my coat pockets under the blankets and thought about the Fourth of July in general and this one in particular. This one in particular, of course, was easily distinguishable by the fact that the temperature was stuck in the middle forties and could not seem to get up. I should have got out the mittens, put away with the other woolens for the summer. Summer! Hah!

Ordinarily, however, the Fourth in our part of Connecticut was warm enough; some years it was quite hot. As for July 4 in general, I wondered if the chief difference between men and women was not that one loved to shoot off firecrackers and one did not. I could not ever remember

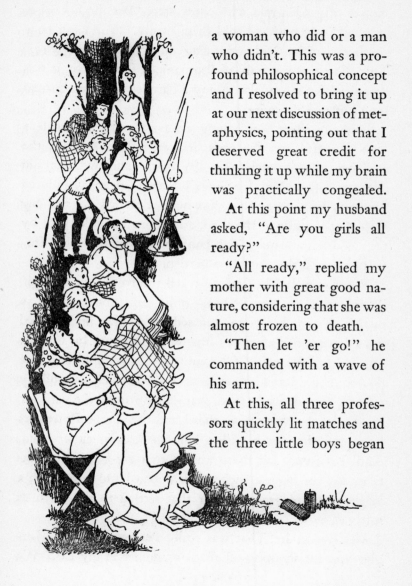

a woman who did or a man who didn't. This was a profound philosophical concept and I resolved to bring it up at our next discussion of metaphysics, pointing out that I deserved great credit for thinking it up while my brain was practically congealed.

At this point my husband asked, "Are you girls all ready?"

"All ready," replied my mother with great good nature, considering that she was almost frozen to death.

"Then let 'er go!" he commanded with a wave of his arm.

At this, all three professors quickly lit matches and the three little boys began dancing around with a sparkler in each hand, shedding a shower of golden rain with every step. "Put the hot wires in a pail," my husband told them firmly. "You can't have another sparkler without giving up a burned-out wire." This affair was not only well-organized for display, it was organized for safety also. Many a bare leg has been burned by a hot sparkler wire.

Suddenly there was a long z-z-z-z-z, a rocket made a high, graceful arc, the ends dripped golden flowers, the audience appropriately said "A-a-ah!" and we were in darkness again. Not for long, however. A many-colored fountain was next, and pinwheels fastened to the big maples at the side of the yard, and Roman candles held by the children, not quite high enough, so that they shot forward toward the vegetable garden.

Not a very lavish display, to tell the truth, but enough. There weren't many duds—only one rocket, and a couple of pinwheels that refused to revolve but spurted out sideways like an angry dragon sticking out his tongue. We obliged by many Oh's and Ah's, the children came politely and offered us sparklers to hold which we politely refused, they danced a great war dance around the yard for the finale, the three boys ahead and the Three Professors following after, each with a long sparkler in either hand. And at the very last there was another z-z-z-z, louder this time, and the biggest rocket shot upward and burst with a bright red and green shower that settled to the earth as softly as snow.

Mrs. Joe said: "That was really very pretty and I forgive you for shooting off that firecracker in my ear." We all agreed. It had been thoroughly charming. I decided I liked the Fourth of July after all.

We struggled out of our blankets and walked to the door. The boys were still dancing.

"Now watermelon!" cried the littlest one, and the cry was repeated: "Yes, watermelon! Watermelon now!"

"Great merciful heaven!" Alfred whispered in my ear. "Doesn't that seem a cool dish for a night like this?"

"Why, no," I replied innocently. "We always have watermelon. I've been keeping it on the cellar floor for two days so it will be nice and cold."

In the living room my dear husband, with more forethought than I had given him credit for, had laid a huge fire, with a backlog as big around as my waist. This he sprang to light, and since he was, and is, a famous fire builder, the paper ignited, the old shingles we used for kindling licked up the flame, and before we had piled our coats and blankets and sweaters on the red chest in the hall, there was a magnificent blaze to bring our circulatory systems back to something like normal.

At this point Martha and Mabel, pressed into service for the occasion, appeared with the watermelon. The children were delighted, the adults slightly less so. But watermelon was the traditional Fourth of July party, and watermelon it was. I wondered in what faraway tropical land it had ripened. Nowhere near here, I was sure of that.

Martha and Mabel, however, had more goodies to come—coffee, in a great pot that we could stand on the hearth to keep hot, and a big slab of cheddar. I thawed from head to toe. Mrs. Alfred and Mrs. Joe began to smile happily. My mother looked as contented as a kitten, with her watermelon untouched by her side and her coffee cup already refilled.

"Ho-hum for the Fourth of July," I yawned. "I love it, I really do." I sat down cross-legged in front of the fire, my face reddening from the heat, my insides warming nicely from the coffee. "Especially now that all the bang-bang is over."

At that moment there was a deafening report from the fireplace a yard away from my head, a large piece of stone dropped off the chimney behind the burning logs, and sparks flew out on the rug.

I must have jumped a foot off the ground. My coffee cup flew out of my hand and smashed on the hearth. Except for a smothered laugh from the middle boy, there was a dead silence. I got to my feet and looked around the room. The Three Professors were sitting or standing in various attitudes of guilt and confusion. It was my husband who finally spoke. "I didn't think it would be quite so loud," he said in a meek voice.

"Did you do that?" I asked him. I suppose I must have sounded pretty grim, for Alfred sprang to his defense.

"Now, now, nothing terrible happened, nobody hurt, the roof is still on!"

"And no thanks to any of you that it is," I told him. All three of them came then and knelt before me in mock penitence. It was the same as when I had first seen them that morning, dancing around in the early morning light after the first cannon cracker: they looked so silly! I laughed.

"At least," said Mrs. Joe, when it was apparent that the crisis had passed, "we can be grateful that it's over for this year." She went to Joe and put her hand in his jacket pocket, extracting three two-inch salutes which she placed in her handbag. "Is that all?" she demanded.

"That's all," he told her. "I swear it. But I bet Alfred has a couple." There was a brief struggle, Mrs. Joe being young, strong, and determined. She ended triumphant with one more firecracker each from Alfred and my husband. That was really all.

At that moment we heard a wild scrambling down the stairs and Blackie, the fat chow, dashed for the screen door and plunged out into the night. We laughed cruelly. Poor little thing, he had been up under the bed since dawn, and his natural needs had at last overcome his terror. The Fourth of July was over at last.

That was a good many years ago, before the war. We don't celebrate the Fourth in the same way now. The little boys have grown up, and two of them lived through their stint in the Infantry and the Air Force. While they were away there was so much shooting going on in the world, not for fun, that the remaining boy who was too young to go and the Three Professors themselves couldn't bear firecrackers.

However, we now have a community picnic at the lake and we all pool our fireworks and set them off out on the float, where nobody is in danger and almost everybody, including the Three Professors, is a spectator. But even this procedure has, we discovered, its hazards. A year or so ago a well-known critic and editor, who is a member of our summer community, was elected to be in charge of the display. The rockets and Roman candles and golden fountains and so on were all piled on the float and we were finishing our fried chicken on shore, waiting for the show. The well-known C. and E. rowed out to inspect the pile. While he strolled around the float something happened —as the forest-fire warnings say: "Did *you* drop that *match!*" Or perhaps it was spontaneous combustion. We shall never know. At any rate the whole show went up at once, mostly horizontally, with rockets shooting in all directions, including shorewards! It was one of the wildest Fourths of July ever seen in New England. The Three Professors would never, on any account, have permitted such a fiasco.

4. *Martha's Garden*

THE road in front of our house in Connecticut stops just beyond the yard. In the horse-and-buggy days it used to be the main road to the next town, and the old stone culverts are still in good working order to prove it. But now it is a grassy lane for a little way until it disappears into the woods. Since nobody goes up the lane past the house we leave the car at the top of the road and call it the "parking." For a good many years the boys —our official lawnmowers—included the parking in the lawn and kept it cut. But for some reason the side of the road and the bank to the stone wall opposite the house were allowed to grow up to weeds and ferns. Just below the weeds was our mountainous leaf pile, where the leaves were dumped at leaf-raking time every fall. I have a bad reputation for excessive neatness, but I never noticed the untidiness of the opposite bank. I had too many gardens to work in as it was. Perhaps I did not look at it. At least, among the many items on my conscience from time to time, this bit of potential garden never figured.

Until Martha came along.

The boys think Martha is the best cook in these parts and I am not disposed to argue. She cleans house with fervor, speed, and unconcealed contempt for all other housecleaners, including me. Ditto for washing, ironing, sewing, canning and preserving, and every modern household task. She has never spun, woven, made candles, or milked a cow—at least not to my knowledge. But I am sure, with the exception of the last, she could if she tried, and she would do it well. She is mortally afraid of cows and thinks little of horses, cats, dogs, and birds in cages.

When Martha came to us she already had had some experience with gardening. Her previous employer, who lived in our town also, had raised the usual vegetables. Martha had been a city child to whom gardens were strange, but she set to with the energy she devotes to all tasks. However, she scorned the usual. Instead of beans and peas, she raised peanuts, or climbing cucumbers, or a thing called spaghetti squash, or Mexican sunflowers. So that by the time she began to work for us she was an experienced if exotic gardener and longed for bigger game and greener pastures on which to try her skill.

For a few years she was content with a small patch I gave her in the upper yard by the lilac hedge. In this she planted all the plants I wanted to thin out and throw away, plus those given her by her friends and mine. The result was miscellaneous but not unpleasing. She had a fine stand of globe thistle, better shasta daisies than I could raise, a couple of big Jack in the Pulpits, the hyacinth bulbs we had given her in a pot one Easter, and many other items which provided a fairly continuous summer of bloom. She did not care for annuals; she wanted plants she could set in the ground and see again next year. But the lilac hedge grew taller and shut more and more sun out of Martha's little garden. It was not enough for her restless soul: she began to look around for other plots to conquer.

It was, I suppose, inevitable that she should turn to the weedy patch opposite the house. It began one year when I was cleaning out the old phlox that had reverted to its original magenta. "Don't throw away those nice plants," she said. "I want them."

"What for? You haven't an inch of room in your garden as it is."

"My garden!" she said with a sniff. "Won't nothing grow there any more. I'm going to put this phlox someplace else."

I went on cleaning out without noticing what she was doing; I simply stacked the pinky-purple phlox in bushel baskets and noticed that after a while the baskets disappeared. I was mildly curious. "Where did you plant that phlox?" I asked.

"Never mind. I planted it. You'll see it next year, and I'll sell you some flowers off it."

"Very likely," I said, and forgot about the matter.

The next spring, when we were all cleaning leaves off the beds on a soft May week end, I noticed that Martha, who had come up with us, was working with the rake by the stone wall opposite the house.

"You don't have to get the leaves off that bank," I said. "It's nothing but weeds."

"That's what you think," she replied briskly. I walked up the bank, my curiosity fully aroused. There under the leaves were green shoots about two inches high, unmistakably phlox!

I did not complain to Martha; one does not complain to Martha. I voiced a few objections to the Professor. "It'll look awful, all that purply phlox right under your nose when you drive up." He was not disposed to take the matter seriously, and truth to tell it did not worry me too much, although now and again, as June wore on and early July, I winced a little when I thought of the magenta row that would presently open.

It did open at the proper season and to my surprise it looked very pretty. Magenta phlox, it seemed, was all right by itself, not complicated by better reds and pinks. I told Martha so and said I liked her new garden. "How much will you give me for a bunch of flowers from it?" she said.

At the end of July I began to separate and reset iris. This is a big job and it meant that I had bushels of rhizomes for which, in the new planting, there was no room. Martha took them. "For your new garden, I suppose," I said. "Who's going to weed the old one?"

"I will if I have time," she told me. "I have to plant this iris now."

She planted iris. She dug up wild flowers from the woods and the roadsides; wherever she went in her car (she bought it several years ago and it makes her independent of us for transportation, which she likes and so do we) —wherever she went in her car she took out the shovel she kept always in the back seat and uprooted plants to bring home with her: columbine and bloodroot, anemone, maidenhair, wild pinks, wild lupine, wild asters, even a clump of pink lady slipper.

"You ought not to dig up those rare wild flowers," I protested.

"Rare!" she said. "I got these in Massachusetts, in a place that was full of·them and little children dragging them out to make bouquets. I should think you'd rather have me dig one of them nice and careful and put it in my garden where it'll grow." It did grow, too, far better than the clumps I bought from a nursery.

Perhaps it was because the spot of earth she chose had never been planted before, and was under trees where the leaf mould had been forming for a hundred years. At any rate, the plants in Martha's garden really thrived. "You've got all those foxglove," she would say. "I should think a lady with a bed full of foxglove could spare some for a poor woman with a new garden."

"Foxglove needs space and sun," I would answer, "but take one, greedy. It won't grow, but what do you care for that?" And of course it did grow, nicely. Or rather *they* grew; Martha did not take one. Instead: "Oh, look at this big clump that came up," she would say. "I guess I'll have to take them all. Can't put them back, can I?"

The first year of Martha's garden, she planted violets besides the iris. Years before the local doctor's wife had given me a few clumps of blue and white violets. I put a row at the back end of the yard under an apple tree and they are now all through the grass. I put a few by the kitchen door and have been pulling them out ever since. When Martha begged for violets I warned her: "You'll be sorry, unless you just want a big violet bed!"

She said she would risk it. "You don't want violets because you've got so many other plants. I haven't anything but phlox and iris. I want to fill up space."

For a long time she struggled with the violets; I could not persuade her to thin them out, although they were spreading everywhere as I had prophesied. (They are awfully pretty in the spring, when the flowers are out and the leaves are small.) But after a while she brought herself to pull out a plant here and there and set it at the lower border of her garden, thus merely transferring the problem and forcing us to move the leaf pile still farther from the yard. She gave violets away. At last she broke down and came to me with a basketful of them. "I can't use these," she said pitifully. "If I bring my friends another violet they won't speak to me any more. You take them." She said this knowing full well that I would put them in the incinerator—not, of course, on the compost pile where they would take root, grow, and start a new bed in all directions.

In a few years Martha had perhaps two dozen varieties of iris, the violets, kept in some kind of control, the long row of phlox, the wild flowers, a lot of bulbs I had given her, and every sort of perennial she could beg or borrow except delphinium which she refused because it had to be sprayed regularly. She had also terraced the bank down from the stone wall, building it up where necessary with rows of stones set in with wonderful artistry, and planting sedums and myrtle to drip down off the barriers she had erected between levels.

She is a feverish transplanter. "You know those canter-
bury bells up in the corner of my garden," she says. I nod.
"I moved them," she adds. "I know," I say. "Of course.
You are always moving things." Or another time: "Those
shasta daisies your sister gave me are getting nice big
roots." "How do you know that?" I ask her although I
know the answer. "I pulled them up and looked," she
says. "I'm not going to have plants in my garden that
don't earn their keep. They've got to grow and keep on
growing." The odd thing is that despite the unorthodoxy
of her gardening methods, that is just what her plants do.

The results of all this hard work, natural talent, and
love are several. First, friends who drive up to the house
say they have never seen the place looking so well—
"Maybe it's because of that wonderful new garden in the
road. When did you start that?" I have to explain that I
did not start it; nay, I resisted it, to no avail. Second,
when the men are carrying leaves in the fall, off the beds
and out of the yard, they have to walk considerably farther down the hill to the leaf pile with their loads. Third,
we have another garden bed to rake off in the spring, and
since Martha will consent to come up to the country only
one spring week end, the raking usually falls to our lot
when we are up to our ears in rakes as it is. Finally, there
is no way of telling where Martha's garden expansion
will end. I can imagine a day when her garden will extend all the way down the hill, past the cottage where my
mother used to live, a third of a mile to the main road. We
shall spend all our gardening hours raking her leaves,
pulling out her weeds, transplanting her plants, because
the garden will by then be much too big for one person to

take care of. The road to our house will be beautiful beyond all our imaginings. And I shall be obliged to do the cooking and housecleaning, because Martha won't have a minute. As it is, she says plaintively that she could scout for many more plants and set them in and move them around if she did not have to stop all the time and do general housework.

Nevertheless, Martha's garden is a pretty sight—in spring when the columbine is red and the violets are purple, yellow, white, and blue; in June with the iris, my tall lavender, some red she borrowed from a friend, my sister's white, the yellow and purple that came from my mother's garden, and so on. The bleeding heart and the white campanula bloom almost all summer. The phlox is developing a variety of its own, with white on lavender, and red inside pink, in addition to the magenta. In the late summer she will have a few yellow marigolds blooming—her one concession to annuals —and the wild asters and the red berries of the barberry in the corner and blue scabiosa (perennial) and the maidenhair, thick and green still. There are no weeds, the stones are set in neat contour rows, the terraced effect rises to the stone wall with a vista of the meadow beyond edged by the Professor's study and the pond; the big maples, which should cast too much shade for Martha's garden and somehow do not, stand guardians over it. I shall never admit it out loud, but I think putting a garden there was a good idea after all. Only I pray, I do earnestly pray that it never gets any bigger.

5. A Child Can Tell the Difference

IN former summers, when the boys were growing up, I used to work in New York in July and September and come up to see my family week ends. I remember one Friday night when the three, meeting me at the train, were excited and mysterious. "We've got a surprise for you," the older boy said. "A surprise," his brother echoed. "Won't tell!" He shut his eyes and his lips tight and shook his head from side to side to show how he could not, on any account, tell. I looked at the Professor. "Some calamity?" I hazarded.

He shook his head also. "Wait and see," he said.

They told me to shut my eyes and with a boy holding to each hand, I was led out behind the barn. They stopped me. "Don't look!" they said. "Now, look!" I opened my eyes and there at my feet was a round, gray-white mass about as big as the bottom of a bushel basket.

"Do you know what it is?" they cried. "Do you? Did you ever see one before? It's a puffball. Isn't it funny?" I admitted that this was the first puffball in my experience and the Professor, who had seen plenty of them as a boy, declared that this specimen was easily twice as big as any he had ever found before. We let the puffball alone, and presently it cracked and darkened and the boys jumped up and down on it, finding that it was a hollow shell from which gray dust flew.

It was Martha who told us puffballs were edible. "Taste like steak and mushrooms both," she said (obviously the forerunner of the shmoo). "You fry them in butter." "*You* fry them in butter," I said. "I don't want any part of them."

I stuck to this position for a long time. During the summer we were likely to find one or two puffballs, usually near the barn, and they would grow and grow and pass through their white firm stage and their gray-black, crackly stage, and return to dust. Once in a while Martha would pull one up when it was young and give it to some friend to cook, always describing in glowing terms how wonderful it tasted. I did not exactly shudder, but I was not going to begin eating puffballs at my time of life.

It was an excessively dry summer that at last won me over. Dry weather, it seems, causes fungi to grow in profusion. The puffballs began to appear in the grass just beyond the kitchen door. Every morning we would find two or three small white buttons in the lawn and in a few days they were as big as dinner plates and still growing. Veteran mushroom fanciers came from miles around to marvel at the size of our puffballs. There were plenty to marvel at, to give away, and to eat, too.

Martha ate them regularly. Once I watched her prepare the stuff for the frying-pan. She had quartered a medium-sized puffball. The inside was snow-white, spongy, but firm; it smelled rather pleasantly of decay—not slimy, putrid decay, but honest mortality. I did not mind the smell, and the feel of it was somehow right. When I pressed my thumb into it, it sprang back as if it had not decayed much, not yet. Martha was slicing it and putting the big white slices in hot butter. "Taste it," she said. "You're not a baby. Only babies won't taste things. Just take a little bite." With some loathing, I put a forkful into my mouth. To my surprise it did taste like both steak and mushrooms. I had evidently been wasting a lot of time not eating puffballs.

From then on we had puffball slices a couple of times a week. The boys contented themselves with fairly small portions, but the Professor and I were completely won over and said puffballs were the best mushrooms we had ever eaten.

Later that same summer people began talking about how many mushrooms were growing everywhere. A friend of ours said she had even frozen some, just to see if it would work. "Puffballs?" I asked. I knew about puffballs by now. Puffballs wouldn't kill you; I had had four slices for lunch that very day.

"Not puffballs at all," she told me. "Mushrooms—real mushrooms."

"You—you eat wild mushrooms?" I asked in surprise.

"Of course. There are dozens of edible kinds and only a very few inedible ones."

"But the inedible ones," I suggested, "are really quite inedible, yes?"

"Oh, yes, they're poison. You don't eat the poisonous ones."

"No," I said. "No, you don't, I suppose."

We talked about something else after that and I went home, thinking about puffballs and mushrooms. I remarked to the Professor that evening: "Did you know that the Reeds are gathering mushrooms from the fields to eat?"

"Don't let me catch you gathering them," he said grimly. "You wouldn't know which were good to eat and which weren't."

"Ellen Reed says it's easy to tell," I protested.

"Easy for her, maybe. I wouldn't touch one of them myself and I wouldn't let you."

"Um-hm," I said, but I was not convinced.

We had a picnic by the pond that evening. Perhaps we had not been there for a few days. Or perhaps the fungi are still close to magic. At any rate, as we brought our baskets along the far side of the pond to the outdoor fireplace, I stopped in amazement. A big maple grows at the

picnic place. There, ringing its trunk, were dozens—I eventually counted eighty-six—fungi that had seemingly sprung up overnight. They ranged in size from buttons to ragged tops about four inches in diameter. They were a bright sulphur yellow with large tan spots or freckles, beautiful but certainly sinister.

We did not touch them, but we walked around and around them in horrible fascination. Unquestionably, if they were edible, they would make a meal for a large family. I resolved to find out something about these mushrooms. The following morning I met Ellen Reed in the village. "Have you got a book about mushrooms?" I asked. "With pictures?"

"I've got several," she replied. "Stop in on your way home and borrow them." I said I would, but for some reason I did not mention the spotted yellow mushrooms we had found by the pond.

That night I began looking at the books, the Professor having previously warned me that, book or no book, he would not eat a wild mushroom and did not expect me to. The first book had a colored frontispiece, and lurid as the colors were, it was plainly our yellow mushroom. Evidently a common variety, I thought. Its name was *Amanita phalloides*. The Amanita part rang a bell in the back of my mind. Amanita—Deadly Amanita; but even I knew that was white, not yellow. I turned to the proper page and read not only the botanical information about *Amanita phalloides* but a racy paragraph about a family which had put a couple of young yellow buttons—just like those by our pond—by mistake into a mess of otherwise honorably edible kinds and died in prolonged agony.

"Those yellow mushrooms," I said to the Professor, "are among the few poisonous ones. I imagine we've got enough out there to take care of all the blue-eyed people east of the Mississippi, if you are interested."

"Leave mushrooms alone," he said.

Nevertheless I read the books. The writer of one of them was contemptuous of the idea that mushrooms were in any way to be feared. The non-edible—he, too, did not call them poisonous—kinds were easy to identify; a child could tell the difference between the good and bad. For instance, the meadow mushrooms, *Agaricus campestris:* you couldn't mistake them. I gathered that it was hard to find a mushroom that wasn't an *Agaricus campestris.* Of course, a couple of branches of the Agaricus family were just a mite undesirable—they wouldn't kill you if you had a stomach pump handy immediately after eating, but you probably ought not to count on going to work the next day. Most of the mushroom books I read, after insisting that nine mushrooms out of ten would not harm a newborn babe, described in great detail the mortal struggles of those unhappy persons who had eaten the tenth one. The worst of it seemed to be that only one "inedible" mushroom in a dish could do the damage, and smothered in cream sauce it would look and smell just like the others. Whether it tasted the same I do not know. Most of the people who tasted it were in no condition to tell.

I did not admit it to the Professor, but by the time I had spent an evening with the mushroom books, I was perfectly willing to be content with puffballs. Incidentally I learned from the book that puffballs never grew larger than a foot in diameter and specimens as large as that were sure to be coarse and disagreeable. I had just eaten three tasty slices of a firm, white, not-in-the-least coarse puffball that was seventeen inches across by my tape-measure. It seemed that the mushroom book authors were in error about puffballs. Hm. Of course to err is human, but about mushrooms, I concluded, it was better to be Superman.

The Professor looked at the colored pictures too, and read the case histories, which merely confirmed his resolution to refrain from eating wild mushrooms and insist that his family do the same. He even became dubious about mushrooms purchased at the grocery. There had been a case, described in one of the books, of an inedible mushroom that grew in the same flat with an innocent group being propagated with all possible care by a commercial grower. "It might happen again," he said. But I refused to be worried to that extent.

In a day or two, when I was about to return the mushroom books, I chanced to walk out by the incinerator. There in the grass were a dozen, almost a fairy ring, of the whitest, roundest, cleanest little buttons I had ever seen. *Agaricus campestris?* I asked myself. A pretty fellow, if it is. It ought to taste delicious. With a paper handkerchief (so thoroughly had the Professor warned me) I broke off a couple and put them in a berry basket. That afternoon I returned the books to Mrs. Reed. "I wanted to ask you about these," I said, producing the basket. "They are growing in our yard."

Mrs. Reed gave my specimens one look. "Deadly," she said. "Deadly. The Deadly Amanita, or Avenging Angel. Beautiful, isn't it?"

I do not know why the two specimens of mushrooms that grow nearest us should turn out to be the most poisonous of all. When I looked again at the pure white buttons of the Amanita, I shuddered. A baby, crawling in the grass, would be fascinated by them. They would come up so easily, too, even to a small child's hand. I went in and got the spade and a newspaper and dug up every one I could find, even though we had no babies. Then I put them in the kitchen stove. It may be that meadow mushrooms are easy to distinguish. It may be that they taste good when creamed or even frozen. But me, I'll stick to puffballs. You can't go wrong on them.

Or can you?

6. What We Can't, We Can

THE vegetable garden has never been my department. On a sunny spring week end, if I do not have too much else to do, the Professor can sometimes persuade me to plant a few peas and carrots and stuff, but my heart is not in it. I greeted with cheers the day when my sons became old enough to help their father plant. This did not represent a distaste for gardening; I enjoy nothing more than to sit on the ground—my knees object to the attitude of prayer and my back to bending over— and engage my fingers and a scratcher in the battle against weeds.

Nor does it mean I dislike vegetables. I like them all, with asparagus at the top of the list, young peas and Golden Bantam corn fighting it out for second place, and the rest crowding along pretty close together. Except for white turnips, which seem to me bitter, watery, and inexcusable, there is no vegetable I don't eat with relish, if it is fresh. I will wash the aphis off Brussels sprouts with strong salt water and enjoy the residue; I love a tomato, just plucked, unwashed, and warm from the sun. Radishes pulled up with some of the June earth still clinging to them cannot be beat. I do not see much reason for okra, but it adds a touch to stewed tomatoes. When the pole beans are about five inches long and a quarter of an inch wide, they melt in your mouth, but don't wait till they have reached their full length and breadth, even though you pull them before they get too obviously pregnant.

Picking vegetables is rather better than planting them. Since most are as good or better raw than cooked, it is a nice way to get a low-calory second breakfast. You pick a handful of beans and before you drop them into the basket at your feet, you eat the two smallest. You poke around in the pungent tomato leaves and find the first half-dozen little yellow cherry tomatoes, and you eat them all, pretending that it wasn't enough for salad anyway. A cabbage leaf is very good under the sun and cabbages and squash are easy to gather, although heavy to carry back to the house. And the filled basket is a colorful bouquet when I take it to the kitchen.

I even enjoy splitting beans or shelling peas. I take the basket, a tray, and a pan out to the yard in the sun. Our latest black cat, Walter Mitty by name because he has four white mittens and is unmistakably a dreamer, chases after a pea hull or pretends to eat a bit of string bean. Various members of the family come by and pass the time of day, usually stopping to grab a handful if it is peas I am working on. Martha, hanging out the wash, makes some observation about my character which is apt but prickly. I am surrounded by the sweet scents of summer, the sun is adding to my tan about which I am a little vain, my brother-in-law, who visits us often but not often enough, reads me bits from the morning paper. This is a good life, I think; I am greatly blessed to be able to enjoy it.

Vegetables are nice, in short, except that they are a bore to plant—and a double, crashing, hideous bore to can! Nevertheless, we can them. Or Martha cans them and I am her reluctant helper. Some day we may have a freezer; I am told that preparing vegetables to freeze is pure joy compared to canning. Some grandchild may replace me in time at the unwelcome task, although why any young person in her right mind would do it, I cannot imagine. I remember the time Martha had a guest staying with her when the beans were ready to can, and I passed through the kitchen a half-dozen times in one morning just for the pleasure of seeing the two of them cutting beans, chattering busily, apparently enjoying themselves, and in no need of my services.

We can vegetables because the Professor always plants twice too many of everything and although we give bushels away to nieces and grandnieces and nephews, there are still many more than we can eat. I do not, of course, like good food to go to waste. I have thought of starting a roadside stand down the hill and using the proceeds to buy a freezer. I have thought of putting a notice in the paper asking all the inhabitants of, say, the Empire State Building or perhaps the Stuyvesant Housing Development to come up and help themselves. Neither of these expedients ever got beyond the dream stage. We shall just have to go on canning. It is true that when we spend winters in Connecticut we are grateful for the filled jars on the shelves. We have learned not to can summer squash—too watery—and the same for broccoli; we never have enough peas or asparagus—too good to eat fresh; boughten canned corn is as good if not better than home-canned. So we limit ourselves to beans, beets, tomatoes, and carrots—a dull lot for a winter evening, if you ask me. But better than nothing and easy on the weekly food allowance.

The procedure on canning beans is that, instead of quickly picking a mess for dinner, you break your back along the whole row if it is bush beans and if it is pole beans you stretch out your arms and ruin your eyes from the sun's direct rays; the basket gets heavier, it looks like enough to feed an army, but you know if you take it into the house Martha will raise her eyebrows and ask if you want to can every day this week. When the basket will not hold another bean, you stagger back with it, wash the mountain of beans in several dishpans of cold water, sit down at the kitchen table, and cut them on a board till your hands are stiff.

Meanwhile the jars are boiling on the stove. When you have a bushel or so cut, you pull the jars out of the boiling water, boiling your fingers in the process, and pack the beans in a jar, adding boiling water to fill and salt if you do not forget it. Then you half seal the top and put the jars into the pressure canner. Thank God for the pressure canner. Time was, in the pre-canner days, when we had to stand over jars boiling in a water-bath for three long hours. The cookbook, I believe, calls for beans to steam in the canner for half an hour, but we have discovered that twenty to twenty-five minutes is long enough. Twenty-five minutes does not seem a long time to spend in purgatory, but you would be surprised!

We cook the beans on the electric stove which gives a good heat but does not respond quickly to changes in temperature. Your aim, of course, is to maintain ten pounds steam pressure; eventually, even on the medium burner, the pressure will climb above ten if you don't watch it. However, if you wait till it is exactly ten and then turn the heat down, the burner will remain hot long enough to drive the pressure up too high. You proceed like a detective trying to prevent a crime before the murderer makes up his mind to use the knife. A little while before the pressure gauge touches ten, you turn down the heat, hoping that although it will go up for a little while, it will not go down too much by the time the burner cools off. I hope I make myself clear. The same sleuthing is necessary for the reverse process; that is, you must raise the heat again before the gauge starts to fall again, so that by the time it falls it won't fall because the stove will be too hot.

Simple?

Yes, it is very simple. All you do is stand by the stove—you can't sit because the gauge is then above eye-level and is not clearly visible—you stand by the stove, therefore, first on one foot and then on the other. Your feet itch, your legs ache, your back gets tired, your eyes blur from close watching of the gauge, you do not care much for canned beans anyway. From the kitchen window next to the stove you can see a patch of green yard and a clump of yellow day lilies waving gently in the sun. It looks so inviting out there, but of course you can't go. You have to watch beans. Twenty-five minutes! It is a millennium.

If anyone knows a shorter, easier, or better way to can beans, I hope I never hear of it. I don't want to know it. I don't want to can beans. I want to freeze them, if the process is really simpler, or throw them away, or stop growing them, or let somebody else do it for me. There were summers, particularly during the war, when I worked in town and poor Martha canned the beans. I know, without being told, that she dislikes it as much as I do, but she is a woman of character. She will not let a string bean get her down. I will, and I don't care who knows it.

Beans, of course, are not the only things to watch. There are other vegetables to can, no more fun either, and a few peaches and plums. Once we had three peach trees, but they winterkilled. We had planted them on the south and lee side of a small chicken house. You are not supposed to do that with peaches, especially in our cold climate. You plant them on the north or windy side of something and they do not get notions about spring on the first mild, sunny day, maybe in February, which is followed by a long period of killing frost. So the peach trees died; but from one of them, below the graft, a runty tree has grown, probably the original peach from which all peaches have been improved. Every spring it puts out delicate pink blossoms, the most pathetically tender of spring flowers. Some of the flowers bear fruit, hard, green, knotty little peaches with brown freckles on them. We do not can these; we do not even eat them. We buy a few peaches to can. The only reason we do not cut the runty peach tree down is that we are fond of it for showing so much grit in a hopeless cause.

Then there is jelly. My older son is a simple lad who cannot get through a meal without jelly for his bread. If

it is not on the table when he sits down he says sadly: "I
suppose the jelly is all gone!" He knows it is not all gone;
he knows he will have to go down cellar after another jar
if there is no more in the refrigerator. He sounds sad because jam yesterday, today, and tomorrow is sweet only
to himself and he would like to share his pleasures.

Most of the jelly comes from an ancient crab apple tree
in the upper yard, next to the vegetable garden. When this
tree is bearing well, as it does every third year or so, we
use, give away, and rake onto the compost heap a good
fifty bushels of apples, maybe more. I am no jelly maker,
but I am obliged to pick up apples, avoiding the wasps
which are likely to be taking bites out of them, and standing upright now and then to rest my back. I cut apples too,
but since I can do this out in the yard in the sun, it is not so
bad. I also spend hours on the telephone, begging friends
and neighbors to come and take a few bushels of apples
away. The Professor cannot bear to think that they are
not being used. When they lie on the ground, thick under
the tree, he comes by, sighs, and says: "You haven't made
any jelly yet, eh?"

"We have made jelly," I say firmly. "We have dozens
of glasses of jelly. We shall make more next week. People
have come and picked up baskets of apples—you were in
your study, you didn't see them. More people are coming
this afternoon. There are just lots of apples; that's all
there is to it."

"O. K., O. K.," he says, warding me off. "I was only
wondering."

Sometimes during the canning season we go away for
the day or maybe for a couple of days. There is no connec-

tion between canning and taking a trip, of course, except that they both occur in summer. When I come into the kitchen after one of these brief absences, I am likely to see, at the back of the kitchen counter, a long row of something covered with layers of newspaper. I peer under the paper and find jars of beans or carrots, or a dozen pints of peaches or plum jam or tomato preserves or dill pickles. They are as pretty as a picture and I know from long experience that they will taste as good as they look.

Martha, however, looks tired. "How are you?" I ask.

"Not so well today," she replies in a small voice. "Will you ask one of the boys to carry those jars down cellar?"

It is canning which has got her down. I know it. It would do the same to me, or worse. Yet we do it every year and are in general glad of the product. I cannot imagine a summer without canning, any more than I can imagine a summer without a vegetable garden. I simply wish it could be done by magic, by remote control, perhaps by those little men who, I am convinced, really run automatic elevators. At any rate, I wish I did not have to do it.

Of course I do not have to. Nobody makes me but myself. Nobody made me pick blackberries last summer. Now, I dislike picking berries, not because of possible wasp stings or snake bites or briar scratches, but because it is so boring. Nevertheless, I picked them. I had company too. Down in my mother's cottage now live my old school friend, the doctor from New York, and her mother. At least her mother lives there all summer, and the doctor comes once in a while for a week end and to spend the short vacation she allows herself from a too-extensive pediatrics practice. Perhaps rashly, she was there in berry picking time and she said she wanted to go with me. We put on old bluejeans, blue denim jackets belted around the waist, and red bandannas tight over our heads. The pails hung from our belts to leave both hands free. The doctor, in some absent-minded doubt of what she was going to do, wore white cotton gloves.

We looked formidable but the costumes were hopefully intended to keep us from being torn by blackberry canes. The strange thing about blackberry briar is not that it scratches your legs as you walk through it but that it will suddenly arch over your head and clutch you in the back with the strength of a fiend. Nobody need tell me berry bushes are inanimate objects. I know better. We stood in the hot sun for hours at a time, and for several days running, because the crop was so big, bleeding here and there and gathering quarts and quarts of berries. The Professor loves blackberries with plenty of cream and sugar. Our younger son loves them even more plain, scorning to put anything on them. But we had far too many to eat. We had trays of them, spread out in the cool spring box in the pantry, where our mountain spring perpetually runs.

"Could you make jam?" the Professor asked. "Nothing better than blackberry jam."

"I never have made it, but I'll try," I said. I began operations on Thursday, Martha's day off—Thursday evening, to be exact. I had spent most of the afternoon painting the scratches on my legs, arms, back, neck, forehead, and so forth with iodine. I looked like the Tattooed

Woman when I finished. So it was after supper when I got out the cookbook to read about jam. With the aid of a sugar thermometer I began to boil the berries and discovered that it takes relatively little time to raise the temperature of sugared fruit to, say, 213 degrees F., but ever and ever so long to get it up three or four degrees higher. Two hundred and seventeen degrees, I decided, was about right. This was based on some calculation too complicated to describe, even if I remembered it. The jam did seem to be getting a bit thick, but I was not sure how thick it ought to be. I found I could get it into the jars all right. However, the next morning, when Martha was in the kitchen looking down her nose at my handiwork, I discovered the jam was roughly the consistency of cement. I chopped it out of the jars, added water, brought it to a boil once more, and put it in the jars again, doing it all with a very professional air as if I had expected to do this part of the operation all along.

Martha was not in the least deceived. "If you had told me," she said distantly, "that you wanted blackberry jam, I would have made it."

"I know. I just wanted to try it for myself. I should have let you do it."

But the Professor was perfectly delighted. He loves my blackberry jam and begs for hot biscuits to put it on. In fact, he talked so much about how good it was that I began to get a little nervous. "*Your* blackberry jam made a great hit," Martha said. "I'll have to let *you* do the jam and jelly in the future."

Now that is the last thing I want. I do not think I shall ever make it again. My mother made the preserves while she

was alive, and she lived long enough for Martha to take over.
I have escaped that part of homemaking. I will do the washing, I will wax the floors, I will polish the brass, but I think
I will never again pick a blackberry. My skin is too valuable
to me and I have no desire to compete with experts in all that
picking berries inevitably leads to.

7. Do Drop In

IN MAY, when we go to Connecticut, it seems that the summer will have no end. Not only will it stretch before us without limits in time, but it will offer us opportunity to do all the things we have been promising ourselves for so long to do. We will take that trip to the shore—we have been saying so for ten years; we will make our first visit to the Adirondacks, we will go back to northern Vermont which we like so much, and so on. There will be a chance to do all of these things: haven't we four long months? And in addition to trips, we will have lots and lots of week-end guests!

In fact, in the flush of the limitless summer, I have mentioned a week-end visit to a number of friends. "You've really got to come up this year," I say. "We've put it off much too long. Of course, bring the children; we've lots of beds. And the dog, too. He can catch woodchucks." From time to time a small warning sounds inside my head; how many week ends do you think there are, it asks gently, even in four months? But I ignore it. We have the whole summer. We love lots of people. We want to see them. We have two guest rooms, and two beds in the playhouse, not to mention the extra bed in the hall. There is no limit to the number we can put up.

That is what I think in May.

Of course we don't want to take trips in June—or have guests, either. After all, we've just arrived, we want to see our old friends who spend the winter, too, in our town, and the garden is demanding. There is an enormous amount of work to do, the boys have to swim and play tennis—even I have to swim now and then. (One of the first signs of middle age I noticed was that I no longer felt I should die if I did not go swimming every day.)

So the long, soft June days go by. We picnic by the pond, we pick the first peas and sometimes the first beans, we do a little painting and a little carpentry, I make a new set of curtains. We celebrate the Professor's birthday with a party, and go to a couple of square dances at the lake. And the first thing you know, with a suddenness that must have no parallel in nature, it is the Fourth of July!

These days on the Fourth we join the other branch of the family also in our town, and there are eighteen and twenty grownups and children for cocktails or hamburgers or to play the Game in the evening. The Fourth is invariably great fun, but after it is over we naturally tend to relax a little. "Nice to have just us four again," the Professor says as he looks around the supper table. Even the boys agree, and I certainly do. "Want to take a couple of days off and go up to Mansfield?" he asks.

We talk it over. Sometimes we do and sometimes we don't. If he has to go anyway, to lecture in some New

England summer course, we do. If it is just a trip, more than likely we don't. It is nice to stay home. Right now, anyway. Later in the summer, I say confidently. After all, we haven't been here so very long.

Time, as it has a way of doing, passes. The corn is silking, the tomatoes are large and green, the roses and delphiniums are over, and the annuals are beginning to bloom. It is pretty hot in the daytime and we are thankful for our cool nights. And on one of those nights, when it is not so cool and I am wakeful, the calendar comes home to me with rude force: next Wednesday will be the first of August!

It is impossible and yet it is true. Where are all our summer plans? We haven't been anywhere except to Pittsfield a couple of times—an hour away—to dine with old friends. We haven't asked the Smiths or the Martins or the Robinsons. We've simply got to have the Robinsons, because at that cocktail party in May I made such a thing about their coming with the children and the dog. Wonder what a dog will do in the annual bed where I have detected the beginnings of a woodchuck hole? Their children are four and seven. Hm. Well, we have lots of room. And I am very fond of the Robinsons. Not to mention the Smiths and the Martins.

So the August week ends, as usual, are given over to guests. The Robinsons' dog digs only three holes under the marigolds, which probably need cultivating anyway. The Smiths come *with* the Martins and we have a very gay time and they are sweet about going with me to market for the things I forgot—in spite of the carload I bought on Friday morning. Two students of the Professor's turn up, too, on Saturday afternoon, on bicycles, and since they come just before supper on their way North, it is natural for them to spend the night. They cheerfully sleep in the playhouse (four more sheets!).

The third week end in the month is given over to family—my family, this time—five of them in all, plus dog (ten sheets, none for the dog), and the three-year-old niece is as charming and funny as a child can be but she does not eat a bite for two days except the lollipops her father produces out of his jacket pocket at frequent intervals. I bite my lips and tell myself that it is not good to interfere between people and their children; I do, however, produce chicken breast, milk, and bread and butter now and then to tempt her, which they do not. She loves lollipops, especially green ones. They don't seem to do her any harm, either. I might write up this remarkable diet for the American Journal of Pediatrics. It is certainly simple.

Around the middle of the month, the Professor looks up from a letter he is reading. "Do you suppose we might ask the Browns down for a couple of days?" he asks.

The Browns are colleagues of his at the University, I do not know them very well, and Mrs. Brown, like so many faculty wives, is almost reproachfully serious in demeanor—she also wears pince-nez and combs her hair the same way she did in college, some time back. However, Professor Brown is a darling, with a beguiling crooked smile, and though his jokes are literary they are quite good. I say: "Of course, the Browns. It will be fun."

The Professor looks at me and lifts an eyebrow. "Well, perhaps," he says, "but anyway, I'd like to ask them." It is wonderful to be as truthful as he is and at the same time not impolite. I wish I could cultivate the art. I also hope the laundry comes back; it is two weeks late now and there are limits to our sheets.

The Browns accept with alacrity for the last week end in the month. On Thursday one of our oldest and dearest friends, a student of the Professor's when he was young and green, calls up and asks if he may drop in Saturday. By the tone of his voice I gather that he would love to be asked for over Sunday. I ask him because I am fond of him, but I wonder about the Browns. The former student is called Ray by his friends, though that is not his name; he is very partial to bourbon, neat; he knows everybody in the theater and has acted in a play or two, though he considers himself only a fortunate amateur. He is a famous storyteller and his stories are not in the least inhibited. I am sure, despite a large acquaintance, that he has never seen anybody quite like Mrs. Brown. Not that he will mind her—she will be a challenge to him. Fetching out two more sheets, I shudder slightly.

And finally, on Friday, an hour or so before the Browns are due to arrive, we have still another addition to our group (sheets: two). The daughter of another old friend is on her way to Canada. May she break her journey with us—just Saturday night and part of Sunday? Will it be too much trouble? She will not think of coming if it is too much trouble, or if there are any other guests. I explain that there *may* be one or two but that we will love to have her and of course she must come. She is a sweet girl, but I can best describe her by quoting my elder son who said she was so pretty it almost didn't matter that she was simple-minded!

I have made Ray's bed in the small guest room on Thursday. Now our younger boy moves in with his brother and I put the last, positively the last two clean sheets on his bed for Eloise. I also shove his clothes over to one side of the closet and put in some extra hangers. And I hastily gather a bowlful of pink and purple petunias for her dresser; petunias are the easiest flowers to arrange if you are in a hurry and I am! The two guest rooms are gay with flowers that took more trouble: dark red dahlias and white nicotiana for Ray, and for Mrs. Brown a dashing tall vase of big zinnias, tall gladioli, and feathery asparagus fern. I was tempted to make her a prim, round, regular little bouquet that would exactly match her character. But I remember that I do not like to be confronted with my character and I imagine Mrs. Brown does not, either.

I have made a cheese ball rolled in chopped pecan meats to go with the cocktails—I'll have sherry for Mrs. Brown, of course—and have picked and cut the beans and gathered and washed the lettuce and done a number of other small chores too trivial to mention but they do take a lot of time. As the Browns' car rolls up the hill and stops in front of the house, I am coming out with the ice bucket. Nice timing, I tell myself. The Professor, of course, has not quite finished dressing, but he shouts down to them from the bedroom window (which seems to startle Mrs. Brown somewhat) and I do the honors.

Professor Brown is friendly, easy, and obviously glad to be here. I think Mrs. Brown is glad, too, but she was brought up in Boston and considers it vulgar to indicate pleasure openly. By the time we have walked to the garden chairs and are seated the Professor joins us, the men begin to talk about books, and I ask Mrs. Brown if she would like to see the garden. She is very polite about it, displaying considerable knowledge of botanical names at which I am not so good; but instead of looking at my garden she tells me about hers: *her* zinnias are four feet high and as big as dinner plates; *her* roses haven't stopped blooming all summer; *her* petunias are the large ruffled sort (I hate them myself); *her* marigolds have been in bloom for weeks (I just don't believe this!); and she doesn't have the slightest trouble raising salpiglossis (I don't believe this, either).

By the time we get back to the chairs, I have developed a hearty dislike for Mrs. Brown. I go in for the cocktail tray, almost resolved to forget her sherry, but hospitality triumphs. I bring the tray, sherry, cheese ball, and all: all, being the makings for Manhattans, at which I rather fancy myself. The Professor never mixes drinks, but since he is expert at entertaining the guests by delightful conversation, I cannot complain.

I might have saved myself the trouble of the sherry, for Mrs. Brown declines all alcoholic beverages with a frosty dignity and even refuses tomato joice or a Coca Cola. Her husband looks happy when I give him his first cocktail and looks at his wife before refusing his second. There is a whole shakerful going begging, but just as I am resolved to drink it myself and forget Mrs. Brown, our sons arrive and save me from disgrace. At this point, for some reason, I remember Ray and his appetite for bourbon. I giggle for no apparent reason and Mrs. Brown of course thinks I am drunk. I become very serious and make a brilliant observation about the book under discussion which causes my husband to smile at me fondly and Professor Brown positively to beam with approval. Mrs. Brown does not beam.

It is a rather heavy evening. The boys depart for a square dance after dinner. The Professor and I had been asked to the square dance, too, and he suggests that perhaps the Browns would like to go and look on, even if they do not wish to dance. Although he is of a sanguine temper, I have never seen him more at a loss for words at the firm incredulity of Mrs. Brown's refusal. So of course we do not go to the dance either, but we sit in the living room and talk—or the men talk and the wives dutifully listen, except that now and again Mrs. Brown remembers some other advantage of her garden over mine and tells me, *sotto voce*. It is too hot to sit inside, really, but Mrs. Brown's hay fever is made worse by the night air. I bring in iced tea as a concession to her temperance principles but she never takes iced drinks.

By ten o'clock I can hardly keep my eyes open. I am probably dying of boredom. I make an excuse and go out into the cool yard. The moon is up and sheds a pale blue light over the perennial border, and the grass, newly cut, and the corner of the playhouse where white phlox is ghostly fragrant. I have seen this yard under this moonlight so many warm summer nights, so many sharp nights in spring and fall, and even a goodly number in winter when the moonlight is pearly white on snow. I love the yard, and its sweet familiarity not only wakes me up but gives me fresh courage. When I go back to the house I am the equal of two Mrs. Browns and I hold out valiantly until eleven-thirty, which is evidently her bed-time, because she gets up, yawns daintily behind her hand, and asks permission to retire. Not alone, however; her husband stops in the middle of a sentence and accompanies her as if pulled by an invisible string.

My husband comes out into the kitchen with me to help wash up the iced-tea glasses. I try to think of something tactful to say, because, after all, Professor Brown is very nice and I am glad we asked him, but all I can think of is Mrs. Brown and her hateful garden. However, my Professor does not seem to notice my failure to make conversation. I wipe off the drainboard and put out the light just as he sets the last glass on the pantry shelf. He takes my arm as we start back to the living room. "Awful woman," he says, but I am sure he does not mean me.

Saturday evening I shall long remember. The day had been lived through well enough; we took a brisk walk in the woods—in spite of the heat, Mrs. Brown was not one to stroll—we drove through the stand of towering, first-growth pine and hemlock which is one of the sights of the town, we stopped by the lake and gave Mrs Brown an opportunity to raise her eyebrows at two little girls aged about a year and a half who were paddling in the water dressed in no bathing suits whatever. But the day was not impossible, there were moments in it of friendly laughter, I grew even more fond of Professor Brown, and the soufflé at lunch was so good that I could even forgive his wife for having been born in Boston. If she was born, and not descended from a broomstick.

The boys went to meet Eloise on the afternoon train. She appeared in a charming pink cotton frock and

changed immediately to immaculate white shorts, which showed that her legs were slender, shapely, and brown. Mrs. Brown's eyebrows became permanently elevated. However, the young people went off to the lake for a quick swim before dinner, I had a little business with the cocktail tray, and there was nothing to do but wait for Ray.

Ray is nearly always late for dinner, which would not endear him to Martha except that he makes over her so charmingly she cannot quite resist him. But this day he is not late. It is six o'clock when he drives up and stops before the house in a long, rakish, cream-colored convertible with the top, of course, down. He, too, is wearing shorts. After all, it has been a very hot ride from town. But Mrs. Brown averts her eyes, as though she had never seen a

man so undressed. I think this is lost on Ray, but I am
not sure. He embraces me with the warmth that is natural
to him; Mrs. Brown is going to wear her eyebrows out, I
fear. Her smile when Ray is presented to her is purely
automatic and disappears at once.

"I suppose I ought to change," Ray says, expecting me
to say Oh no, don't. But I am weak.

"There's plenty of time," I tell him. "I'm just getting
the ice."

He looks at me with reproach in his eyes, but he is an
obedient guest, so he disappears into the house and appears again in ten minutes with his hair wet from a
shower and wearing a linen jacket, white ducks, white
sneakers, and no socks. I wonder if the sight of his bare
ankles is going to be hard on Mrs. Brown, but I decide
I do not care.

"I am dying of thirst," he says with what, for him, may
be no more than the truth. I hand him an old-fashioned
glass containing three ice cubes and about three ounces of
bourbon. He sighs and kisses my hand. "Lovely woman,"
he murmurs, and sits down on the settee beside Mrs.
Brown. She does not exactly move her skirts to avoid
touching him; she is, after all, a lady of Boston. But she
stiffens and clasps her hands hard in her lap. I wonder if
I should begin to be sorry for Mrs. Brown. I decide not.
She should be made to suffer a little—for her garden, if
for nothing else.

Ray is brilliant, well read in current books, and in
general surprisingly well informed. Professor Brown, I
can see, is delighted with him. There is a wary look in
Mrs. Brown's eye. She is confused. She thought he was

a playboy, an irresponsible, probably an alcoholic, and here he is talking like a civilized man, matching information with her own husband in the seventeenth century where he is an authority, and giving no sign of the effects which the large quantities (I have filled his glass twice) of whiskey he is drinking must be having on him.

The children return, Eloise puts on another charming cotton frock, Ray tells her she should not be so beautiful and asks prettily after her mother, and we go in to dinner, he with his fourth bourbon firmly in hand. His step is firm, too. He does not seem in the least intoxicated.

I seat him on the same side of the table as Mrs. Brown, but with my younger son between them. Eloise is across from him, where he cannot hold her hand. Professor Brown is prepared to continue the literary conversation where they left it in the yard, but Ray is tired of literature by now. He begins to talk about his mother. Now I happen to know that Ray is the most dutiful of sons, that he not only maintains his mother in all the luxury she will accept, but that he never lets a day pass without telephoning her, sending her flowers, or calling on her. Mrs. Brown does not know this. So when Ray tells a story about his mother which makes her out a flibbertigibbet, an incompetent, without a grain of common sense, I can join in the laughter because the story is really very funny, but Mrs. Brown cannot. Disrespect to His Mother is added to Drinking Enormous Quantities in her category of Ray's sins.

When Ray finishes his story he leans forward, around my son, and smiles sweetly at Mrs. Brown. I know the worst by now. He is on to her. Ho-hum. It is now seven-thirty. Four hours to go before she must retire. Thrones have toppled in four hours. Mrs. Brown does not even attempt to smile in return. Her back is stiff as a ramrod, she can hardly lean forward to eat her soup. It is going to be an interesting evening.

I do not know at what point my husband became aware of the situation. Professor Brown, poor man, never did. He laughed till the tears came to his eyes at Ray's stories about his seven aunts and six uncles who had helped bring him up. (Making Fun of Family—only a step below Disrespect to Mother.) After the third aunts-and-uncles episode, when the eldest uncle was trying to teach Ray's mother, his sister, how to drive a car in traffic, my younger son got up to refill Ray's glass. No protest. Eloise was gasping and holding her sides. "I hurt!" she said. "I can't laugh so much!" She looked at Mrs. Brown as she spoke and gasped again, this time not from mirth. Eloise, as I have indicated, is a sweet but simple soul. It was incomprehensible to her that anyone should be registering so much distaste for what seemed to her so delightful.

Ray did not look at Mrs. Brown this time, but he caught the astonishment on Eloise's face and knew she was looking at Mrs. Brown. He took a long draught of the bourbon and figuratively squared his shoulders. The battle was on, and he was more than ready for it.

During what was left of dinner and much of the evening which followed, I have never seen a finer exhibition of virtuosity. Ray told story after story, about the great and near-great in the theater and in Hollywood, about a half-dozen of the most important people in Washington, about top figures in the academic world, including the president of one of our largest universities. They were not quite outrageous stories, not quite malicious, not nearly so bawdy as Ray might have been. The young people, the two professors, and I found them inexpressibly fascinating. And Ray listened, too. He listened to Professor Brown's joke about seventeenth-century poetry, he listened to my husband's account of a dignified colleague who, in the midst of a lecture, had been intimately attacked by a bee, he told Eloise she was as beautiful as the most beautiful of the young movie actresses, and then he launched into a tale about that same actress which made us weep for joy again.

Nor did he neglect Mrs. Brown. To her he behaved like the most accomplished courtier of the old school. He brought a cushion for her back, he adjusted the light so it would not shine in her eyes, he offered her a drink, any kind she could name, hot or cold, he asked her if she felt a draft, he deferred to her before expressing a literary opinion. Professor Brown, I could see, was as much captivated by Ray's charming manners to his wife as he was by his powers as a raconteur. The professor, I began to fear, was singularly unresponsive to his wife's moods; he was henpecked and he didn't know why. For Mrs. Brown did not relent, she did not yield, she was not in the slightest degree won over, and she was not amused. Ray for her was all that she had feared when she first saw him coming into the yard wearing shorts. Every word he uttered merely confirmed her in her opinion.

About ten o'clock Ray began to tire of the game; and Eloise was very pretty. So he came and sat on the floor beside her, leaning his arm across her knees, and began a conversation that became more and more murmurous. Eloise had known Ray all her life and he was twice her age. She had probably always thought of him as her parents' friend, a very funny man. But Ray can be gallant when he chooses, and tonight he chose. Perhaps he was a little drunk, not only on the bourbon but at the challenge of Mrs. Brown. At any rate, he was on the point of behaving rather disgracefully, particularly since Eloise did not have sense enough to stop him, when my husband firmly took the situation in hand.

"I'm going to take you for a ride," he said. "A short ride, just a couple of miles, and show you something you've never seen before." His voice was clear and raised a little. Ray stopped stroking Eloise's arm and turned his head to listen. "You'll see a house that looks as though nobody had lived in it for years: the paint has almost worn off, the grass isn't cut, nobody has picked up the big branches that have fallen, the shades are drawn—all but one!" Ray was really listening now, and so, I was pleased to see, was Mrs. Brown. "All but one . . . and at that one sits a man with a shotgun! And at each corner of the house there is a big electric bulb fastened below the second-story windows that lights up the yard as bright as day." He stopped a minute. "Want to go?" he asked.

Ray got up and dusted off his knees. "Why?" he said. "Why the lights, why the shotgun, why the unkempt yard? Of course we want to go."

I excused myself, on the ground that the car would be full and that I had seen the Stearns's yard before and it depressed me. But the others went. Mrs. Brown might

have demurred, but my husband made a point of insisting
that she go. My older boy, who is clever in the same way
his father is, took Eloise's arm, and although she had been
bemused by Ray, she preferred the society of a man of her
own generation. Professor Brown brought up the rear
with Ray. They were back to the seventeenth century,
batting around a theory about the Restoration poets.

When they had gone I drew a long breath of relief.
Thank heaven that was over. Thank heaven I had a husband who could not only see a difficult situation but re-
lieve it. There was a small quantity of bourbon in the
bottle. Without bothering to get a glass or ice, I tilted the
bottle and drained it. It was an extremely short drink, but
I laughed aloud to think what Mrs. Brown would do if
she had seen me.

As I tidied the room I thought about the house with the
floodlights in the yard. A brother and sister live there, both
nearing seventy. He had loved a girl who jilted him; she
had married a man who abandoned her with a month-old
baby. Brother and sister and child live out the years in the
family place. They feel that the town looks down its col-
lective nose at them. More and more they withdraw from
the life around them. For fifteen years now they have not
stepped out of the house. They are besieged, or so they feel.
The lights go on at night to keep prowlers away—what
prowlers, only they can say. The shotgun is to protect them
from unwelcome visitors; nobody has wanted to visit them
for a long time. Their food comes by mail; if it were delivered by the grocery truck it might be poisoned. And so
on. A sad, strange, rather typical New England story. Ray
will understand it because he understands every queer road

the human heart takes; I wonder what Mrs. Brown will make of it. But she comes from Boston—and that is New England, too.

When they return, they talk of nothing but the Stearnses. Even Mrs. Brown is fascinated by the house and the lights. Ray is now on his best behavior, the young people leave to catch the end of a party at the lake, and the balance of the evening is quite peaceable. My husband holds the conversation steady; he never lets it get out of hand. It is almost twelve o'clock when Mrs. Brown recollects herself, and with a visible start rises and makes her good nights, her husband meekly accompanying her. She does not quite ignore Ray; she has not forgiven him, but her attention has been temporarily distracted. She bends her head slightly in his direction as he bids her good night.

When they have gone upstairs, the three of us, without a word, go out into the yard. Ray has another bourbon and my husband and I join him. "I have been a very bad boy," Ray says with mock meekness, as he squeezes my arm.

"You certainly have. I shall die ten years sooner because of this evening," I tell him.

"You will never die," he says, and stretches himself out on the grass, under the moonlight.

Nothing unusual happened on Sunday. Eloise was called for shortly after lunch by the friends with whom she was driving. Ray left a half-hour later, with fond thanks to the Professor and me and with Professor Brown's cordial invitation to lunch with him at the University. Mrs. Brown did not unbend at all. He was not her kind of man, and I guessed that the lunch invitation might be long in coming. The Browns stayed on to supper, although I had not quite expected them and had to improvise a meal. They left at eight or so and I went in to refill the ice bucket, since the night was still warm. As I came out carrying it I must have looked tired, because the Professor walked quickly to me and took it out of my hand.

"How many times have you carried that across this yard?" he said tenderly.

"How many indeed," I answered. "But it's August, and in August we have guests for the week end."

8. Don't Wait to Buy a House!

IT IS hard to remember the time when we did not have the farm in Connecticut. Indeed, the Professor and I were married only a short time—a year and a day, to be exact—before the farm was, in a manner of speaking, ours. During that first year we drove around the suburbs near New York in our Model-T Ford runabout (a mighty nice little car and if I could I'd go out and buy one tomorrow), looking for possible summer places. We did not want to commute; commuting has always seemed to me neither fish nor fowl, with the disadvantages of both the city and the country and none of the advantages of either. (I know, of course, that many people disagree with me.) What we wanted, even then, was a place we could go to for week ends in the spring and fall and could live in during the long summer vacation. All the places we looked at were too suburban, too up-to-date, and far too expensive. Anything was too expensive for us. Our bank balance at the time was slightly over two hundred dollars. I do not know why we thought we could buy a country place—the bounding optimism of youth, perhaps. Or perhaps we were just looking.

We had determined not to follow the various members of our families into the country communities in which they were already established. Start on our own, we told ourselves. But we were very happy to accept the invitation of the Professor's brother to spend Labor Day week end at his farm in Connecticut. We knew it was a nice town. We just felt we ought to settle down somewhere else. When we arrived at the farm the Professor's brother and my mother, who was staying there also, announced that they had found the perfect country place for us, in the north part of town.

We looked skeptical. This was against our principles. "Is it for sale?" the Professor asked with what, for him, was rare practicality. They didn't know; they hadn't asked. They had just driven up this dirt road and there was this house, a nice little house, a bit out of repair of course, and wonderful maples in front of it and a big rock in the field opposite. "We'll take you to see it first thing tomorrow morning," the Professor's brother said.

"We'll go," said the Professor, very politely. "It sounds fine. All we need is money."

Everybody laughed and it was agreed that we had best go and look at our prospective new home by ourselves. It was in a part of town unfamiliar to us, but we were given careful directions and had no trouble in finding the road. We came down a long hill past a first growth of tall pine, straight as masts, two feet through. Beyond the pines the road flattened out into a Hollow with a creek meandering through it and the hills on either

side softly folding it in. Rather nice. "Our" house was on
the far side of the Hollow, with a small shingle cottage at
the point where the dirt road up the hill met the Hollow
road, then unpaved. In front of the cottage a grizzled
little man was sitting on the bench by the door, smoking a
pipe. He looked at us as we drove by but made no answer
to my timid hail.

The fields on either side of the dirt road were in various
stages of cultivation; we passed ripening corn, a couple of
pastures with cows feeding, a field of millet, a patch of
potatoes. The road rose gradually to a big white barn, and
then with a sharp rise it leveled out to the house. It was a
smallish house, a story and a half, with three dormers in
the big roof above the front windows. As we stopped the
Ford and got out we could see that there was one extension
at right angles to the main house and another leading out
from that. It looked shabby, and although there was a wire
fence around the yard, there was no lawn, only a patch,
here and there, of weedy grass.

We had learned the name of the owner, so the Professor asked the young woman who came to the door if she was Mrs. Thomas, and if her husband was at home. He came to the door behind her and said good morning.

"We wondered about the place," the Professor said. "Would it be for sale?"

Mr. Thomas rubbed his thumb along his chin. "Might be."

"Could we—could we look around?" I asked.

"How much are you asking for it?" the Professor said gently.

"Five thousand dollars," said Mr. Thomas, in a voice that was louder than necessary. I suspected that he was surprising even himself by the figure he named. Neither the Professor nor I said anything. There was not much we could say, considering the state of our bank account.

Mr. Thomas took our silence to mean we were waiting for him to make another move. He did. "Take you around, if you like," he said. "Come in."

The house did not impress me greatly at the time. There was what had once been a big kitchen with a fireplace, but the old chimney had been removed. There were two square rooms in the front with an entrance hall between. The two extensions were in pretty bad shape. Off the old kitchen (which the Thomases used for a sitting room) at one end was a milk room and at the other end the traditional kitchen bedroom, the birthing room. There was a quantity of fresh brown oatmeal paper on the walls and the woodwork was mustard yellow with squiggles. We did not go upstairs.

No, when I thought about it the next day I was a little

vague about the house. I thought it would do, it would need a lot of work but I didn't mind that, it had "possibilities." One thing interested us in the back room the Thomases used for a kitchen: into an iron sink an iron pipe poured a never-ending stream of clear, cold water. "Don't you turn that water off?" I asked. It had splashed a good deal and the floor under the sink was wet and rotten.

"It's a good spring," Mr. Thomas said. "Best in these parts. The old people lived in this house more than a hundred years and used that well in the yard, but they had the spring piped in about 1900. Comes from up in the woods, couple of hundred feet higher than the house. Hasn't stopped running yet."

I was too ignorant about houses and their water supply to think much about this. I merely noted that I should turn the water off. That it was desirable to have a gravity flow of water which did not stop coming did not occur to me, so inexperienced a city child was I. If the Professor was any wiser, he did not mention it. But in general, while we were buying our house, our good fairies were in constant attention on us. We needed them.

After we had seen the house Mr. Thomas took us out back, to the meadow that led down into the Hollow. The hay had been cut and the new grass was thick and green. There was a tumbledown sap house at the foot of the meadow, and then a patch of woods. "White pine," said Mr. Thomas, "self-sown, about fifteen-twenty years old. Biggest stand in this part of the state."

We entered the warm, still pine grove, the trees twice as high as the Professor's head. Mr. Thomas had gone on in front a few paces. I pulled the Professor's sleeve. "I bet you could get it for four thousand," I said. My husband looked at me with a distant stare, as if he were walking in his sleep, but he made no reply.

We went on through the pine woods, stepping over maidenhair and Christmas fern, and a carpet of pine needles soft under our feet and sweet where we trod on them. There was a sort of path and presently it opened out into a cleared space where two ancient, knotty maples made a magic ring into which the pines had not stepped. We turned to the left past the big maples, walked between a couple of young hemlocks, and were in another world! It was a hemlock forest, dark, cool, high. Nothing underfoot but the hemlock needles and an occasional rosy mushroom or orange fungus. Nothing overhead but the waving feathers of the hemlocks and the blue September sky. The Professor seized my arm. "I must have this place!" he whispered fiercely.

About love at first sight, on those rare occasions when it occurs, there is nothing to be done. We walked through more woods that morning, past a huge old maple twice the span of the Professor's arms—about fourteen feet. We walked up the brook that made gentle white water falling over rocks. We climbed to the wooden storage box for the spring, its top entirely greened over with thick, soft moss. We saw the ox pasture, named for the pair of oxen that in years gone by had always fed there, its grass smooth and short from Mr. Thomas' cows, and dotted with lichen-covered rocks and juniper bushes on which the berries were blue.

None of these additional allurements made any difference. The Professor had lost his heart, in that mysterious and irrational way in which hearts are always lost, to a spot of earth, a hundred and fifty acres in extent. The house did not matter, the gravity spring did not matter, the high, waving hemlock branches did not really matter. We do not love the loved one for her straight nose or her curly hair, but for what the philosophers call her essence. It was the essence of Mr. Thomas' place that the Professor fell in love with, and the love affair has been going on unabated for more than a quarter of a century.

There was no question, when we got back to the house again, of haggling over money. The Professor did not try to bargain. I do not believe he even remembered that our total wealth, besides the fact that we both had jobs that brought in regular pay checks, was two hundred dollars. Of course we had our health! In a sort of daze, he thanked Mr. Thomas and we got into the Ford again. The little old man in the shingle house was weeding his garden. This time, as we went past, he raised his arm in a stiff, country salute. Perhaps he knew that we were more than casuals driving by. At any rate, that afternoon we came back and greatly to Mr. Thomas' surprise, I am sure, we gave him our check for one hundred dollars to bind a contract to purchase.

An uncle of the Professor's lent us money for a further down payment, and by taking a second job the Professor paid it back within a year. There remained a first and a second mortgage, the latter held by Mr. Thomas' father. There had been a little difficulty about that. The old man, a farmer in a near-by town, had loaned his son a thousand dollars to help him buy his farm a couple of years before, but he was not disposed to extend the loan to a stranger and one from the city in addition.

When the Professor went to call on him he was driving a wagon around his fields, spreading lime. He shook his head at the Professor's proposition, not quite finally but with many doubts. "Do you mind if I sit up beside you while you drive around?" my husband asked. "We might talk about it easier that way." So the two of them drove; the Professor jumped down to open gates—he didn't in the least mind, as old Mr. Thomas doubtless feared he would, getting lime on his trousers or mud on his shoes. The Professor talked about the farm in the Middle West where he had lived as a boy and about a brother who was still a farmer; they talked, I am sure, about everything under the sun, from the weather to dipping sheep. When they had finished, the old man said he guessed he might extend the loan. So it is with a love affair: we know how to behave to secure the loved one for our own. Besides, the Professor has a way with him; he was then and is now, in a deceptively gentle way, a persuasive fellow.

Thus between morning and evening of one day we had a place of our own, we were landowners, we were committed not only to the country but to the particular town in Connecticut which we had resolved to avoid. We learned later that our quick decision was what won us the place— that love affair again; the Professor knew! Or maybe it was our good fairies. Mr. Thomas, it seemed, having named a price considerably higher than he thought he would get, never expected to see us again. He had not really intended to sell anyway, but crops had been poor, he was in debt, things had been going badly with him. He was discouraged that morning when we called on him. And when we came back with our check in hand, he could do nothing but sell. Mrs. Thomas' father, it turned out further, would have been glad to buy the place himself. It was considered a good farm, and the water was exceptional. Mrs. Thomas herself wept for three days after we had closed the bargain. We learned all this years later. Perhaps, if we had known it then, it would have affected our decision, perhaps not. The Professor's love affair was very powerful. I say nothing of my own.

For a long time after we bought the farm and were spending the summers there, Mrs. Thomas used to drive up and see us—no, not us, the place. She would walk across the yard, a green lawn now, and look back at the house, fresh with white paint and new shutters; a new roof, too. "It looks beautiful," she would say wistfully. "We shouldn't ever have let it go!" Her tone wrung my heart; I was sorry for her. Yet for myself, I was glad. I was glad we were there. I was glad it was our house and our farm. As for the Professor, he was simply in love, and with a man in love there is no arguing.

9. "An Interesting Collection of Different Shapes"

ABOVE is what the seed catalogue says on the subject of Gourds: ornamental, inedible. But edible or not, and ornamental or not, beyond question gourds are the Professor's favorite crop. Although I have never succumbed to either habit, I imagine that growing gourds is a little like becoming a morphine addict. You try a little bit at first, with beautiful results; then you take a little more. After a while you are out of control, your will is gone, you have lost wife, child, job, home. The difference between becoming a morphine and a gourd fiend, of course, is that in the latter case you have not, in your compulsion, lost wife, child, etcetera; you have merely gained gourds.

The Professor started slowly. The first year he bought a package of mixed gourd seed, planted them in the ground when he planted the squash and cucumbers, and harvested a basket of yellow, green and white stripes, green and yellow pears, and beautiful white eggs. I admired the result, we waxed them, and they looked pretty in a wooden bowl on the living room table. I did not know that the first dose of the drug had taken hold.

Most of the first crop did not ripen—planted too late in our too short summer. So the next spring I sent the gourd seeds off to a neighbor with a greenhouse, to plant along with a few annuals I always want started early, and by the time we came up to Connecticut in late May, the Professor had two flats of large, husky-looking plants. Our vegetable garden is sixty feet square; I privately estimated there were enough gourds to plant about half of it.

"Are you going to put them all out?" I asked.

"Oh, no. No, not all. I don't suppose I'll plant more than a couple of dozen. Just a couple of dozen, that's what I'll use."

"Oh," I said.

During the next day or so the Professor was busy in the garden. I was busy, too, scratching the annual bed, weeding the perennials, hanging the summer curtains, doing a hundred inconsequential jobs that are part of beginning to live at the farm for the summer. I did not notice what he was doing except that I found, whenever I wanted my flower scissors, they were not on their accustomed nail. I blamed my children. "Which one of you boys borrowed my big scissors and please bring them back," I said.

The Professor hung his head in mock apology. "I'm the boy," he said. "I've been fixing up a little gourd trellis. Want to see?"

I went with him to the vegetable garden. Now, sixty feet square, as any schoolboy will tell you, means two hundred and forty feet of boundary fence. We learned to fence our garden after our first summer, when the woodchucks ate everything but the tomato plants. Two hundred and forty feet of fence. I do not say the Professor had built a trellis along the entire length. Here and there he left a break. But in each corner and extending far along each side he had erected poles just inside the wire, had cut cross-poles, and these were tied with heavy hempen twine to the uprights. He needed my scissors, of course, to cut the twine.

Outside the garden fence were two empty flats. I looked at them and then at him and he hung his head again, looking, as he well knows, very winning, like a small boy caught stealing a pie off the pantry window sill.

"You planted them all," I said. He nodded. "Maybe they won't all grow," I mused hopefully.

I did not know the Professor's mania. Gourds, it seems, grow best on a manure pile. That is, their capacity for absorbing plant food is boundless; they will take any amount of nourishment and grow bigger on it. The Professor did not have a manure pile handy to the garden, but down in the barn we do have the remains of one left long years ago by Mr. Thomas, a working farmer. He carried bushels and bushels of this manure to his gourds. I had noticed him pushing the wheelbarrow up from the barn with a couple of baskets on it, but in my ignorance I thought he might be carrying nourishment to my rose bed.

He also carried water. Gourds like lots of water. Although that was a reasonably wet year, if it did not rain for four or five days the Professor got out the hose and left

it running in the corners of the garden to give his gourds a
good soaking.

I must say the gourds repaid all this attention a hundred, nay, a thousand fold. By the end of June it was evident that they were going to grow and grow and grow.
Several long tendrils were up to the top of the trellis and
beginning to make their way horizontally along the top-
most pole, where they met and mingled with another
branch doing the same thing from the opposite direction.
By the first of August the Professor was out measuring
the amount of growth each day of the end shoots; six
inches was an average day. I am not exaggerating, either. It
would be impossible to exaggerate about gourds. The
fruit was forming, too, and I must say that the variety in
shape and color was endlessly interesting, even to me. To
the Professor—well, keep your mind on morphine and
you will get the idea.

He went out every morning with a big ball of twine
and, of course, my scissors, and tied the shoots firmly
along the poles. He often made me come and see the marvel of the spring-like tendrils that bound the stems to
their supports: the soft, straight, groping antenna; the
slight curve, like a beckoning finger, when the support
was reached; and the curled spring, tighter and tighter,
making the stem firm and sure, practically unbreakable
at last.

We had quite a harvest that year. There were three full
bushel baskets, two half-bushel baskets, and a few odd
ones. We spread the gourds in the September sun, the
Professor washed them in Lysol solution, dried them on
newspaper in the grass, waxed them (all this the proce-

dure recommended by the garden book), and spent a half-day sorting them out to be sent away in batches to family and friends. They were really wonderful and I was glad to have my share, with every possible container full of its complement of shapes in yellow, white, and green.

The Professor was really cooking on all four burners by now and if anybody thought he had exhausted the gourd question by his enormous harvest, anybody was much mistaken. The small, varicolored gourds are annuals. Even with the best of care, they begin to fade by mid-winter in the house and most of them rot by spring. A few will dry out and last for years, like an ancient baby's rattle, making a distant, dry music when shaken.

There is another variety that lasts for centuries, and these were the Professor's next project. The annual gourds have yellow flowers that look like squash blossoms and bloom in the daytime. The Lagenaria, the permanent kind, put out a waxy, orchid-like, mysterious bloom that opens at night. It is the Lagenaria that really do the growing! The first year we had them I made a notation in my diary on August 30: "Gourds are prodigious; the long one is 56 inches." On September 3 the long one measured sixty-one and a half; on September 5 (must have felt tired out) it had progressed to sixty-two; on September 9 it was sixty-five inches long and the Professor took a picture of me standing next to the gourd. We are just the same height, although there the resemblance ends.

One of the delights of the annual gourds was making them take unnatural shapes by tying strings around their middles, putting them, when small, into bottles, or

otherwise torturing them. I never quite approved of these practices. I always felt that the constricting string or glass must have made the little fruit very short of breath. As his addiction really took hold of the Professor, however, he laid aside these childish practices. He was in the business of raising Lagenaria for keeps, and had no time for trivia. Besides the daily tying and strengthening of the trellis, he was busy building the supports higher to keep the mounting vine from falling on its face. I had a feeling that this was a losing game; the gourd would surely grow higher than he could build. But it was not my plant so I said nothing. He also had to measure the daily growth.

The Lagenaria is not harvested in the fall, like the small ornamental gourds. It stays on the vine all winter and in the spring it is dry, hard, and light, and covered with a scaly black skin that has to be removed with elbow grease and steel wool. Once the gourd is cleaned, it emerges a soft blond color, slightly and pleasantly mottled with pearly gray. In shape it is pure Euclid, ranging from a long to a short curve, and the shapes have names: Giant Bottles, Giant Clubs, Sugar Troughs, and so on. There is one, the Caveman's Club, which in its knotty irregularity looks just like that. With a Caveman's Club in one hand and a long-haired woman in the other, the Professor would be equipped for the Stone Age.

After a few years, we had the problem of what to do with the Lagenaria. We made wren houses of some of them and the wrens liked them fine and set up a couple of families every summer in each one. But if there is no limit to the Professor's gourds, there was certainly a limit to the wrens who wanted to nest near our house, or even up in the garden or down in the back lawn. The Professor makes beautiful wren houses, cutting the little neat hole just the size of a quarter, and punching a couple of holes in the top for the suspending wire. The gourd house swings gently in the wind and I am sure the baby wrens think the new housing project is better than the Waldorf. He gave away a number of gourd birdhouses. He made a gourd dipper to hang by the outdoor faucet. He gave away gourd dippers. He hung a handsome bunch of blond Lagenarias on the wall in the corner of the library. He placed several of the most outlandish shapes over the Dutch china cabinet in the living room. In each corner of the dining room, on the upright beam that stands out, he hung one of the most purely beautiful shapes. The Lagenarias are indestructible; our ten-year old dipper is like new.

Still he raised gourds.

The trellis changed. Down the center of the vegetable garden, the Professor erected a double row of stout poles, deeply buried to make them rock-firm. On these he fastened cross-poles, a double arbor. When the gourd vines sent out their yards and yards of rich, green leaves, they climbed and intertwined over this arbor, making a green shade through which we could walk. Until the fruit began to grow, that is; after that, we walked it only in peril of being knocked unconscious by a hanging Giant Bottle or Sugar Trough. Lagenarias when green are about as heavy as their corresponding size would be in oak, and equally hard.

Nevertheless the arbor was a huge success. Dinner guests, before they went home, would be taken on a tour through the arbor and would emerge breathless, a little disheveled, and dumb with astonishment. The Professor counted eighty-five sound Lagenarias that fall in the arbor. Eighty-five big gourds to hang on the vine over the winter, eighty-five gourds to be scraped and polished; eighty-five gourds to be disposed of in some way. I admire gourds. They are undeniably beautiful in color, shape, and texture, they are occasionally useful, the wrens love them. But I could not imagine how we would dispose of eighty-five more in addition to those we already had.

However, the problem was taken care of and in a way that was not happy. At spring plowing time, the Professor wrote young Herbert, the farmer's son, exactly what to do. Knowing the Professor's gift for clarity, I am sure his directions were minute and particular. The arbor was to be torn down. The gourds, dry and hard now, were to be tossed over the fence in a pile. When he, the Professor, came up he would take care of them.

At our first May week end the garden was plowed and the arbor was as if it had never been.

So, unfortunately, were the gourds.

The Professor looked all over. He found one or two broken gourds lying in a corner of the garden but none outside the fence. Yet as he walked through the freshly plowed earth, he kept kicking up pieces of hard shell. That day when we went for the milk we discovered that young Herbert had torn down the arbor all right, but the gourds he had simply plowed under! He had not read that part of the Professor's letter.

Now I did not particularly want eighty-five more gourds; but I was almost as sorry as the Professor that the crop had been ruined at a single stroke. The boys and I tried to console him, but there was not much we could say. He is a man of more than average intelligence. He knows perfectly well that the loss of the eighty-five was not catastrophic. He knows that gourds are limited in their uses, and since they are so big there is a limit also to the space that can be devoted to them as ornament. Nevertheless, he likes gourds; he likes to plant them and feed them and tie them up and fuss with them and see them grow and count and weigh and measure them, and scrub them down to their soft, waxy, bleached-wood tone. The loss of a year's crop, a big crop, an extra-special crop, was a real loss. He tried to laugh it off.

"It was probably a good thing," he said. "God knows we've got enough of them. Maybe it'll cure me. I don't believe I'll ever raise them again."

Of course he did. The Giant Bottles, brothers of the poppy in spirit at least, are not so easily knocked out. A drug is a drug. The plowed-under gourds were hardly cold in their graves when the Professor, with his two sons, was building a new trellis out by the asparagus bed. "A little one," he said. "Just a few plants."

I said nothing. I knew it was not a little trellis; I knew there would be a lot of plants and many, many gourds. But I was not going to complain. If the Professor wants gourds, there is no reason why he should not have them. I can always move out to the old playhouse. And compared with other addictions—he is not an excessive drinker, he does not smoke before breakfast any more, he does not play golf or mix up dangerous chemicals in the cellar, he is definitely not lost to cocaine—no, compared with other addictions, I settle for the gourds. They are clean, safe, decorative in moderation, and they keep him out in the fresh air. He couldn't have found a nicer madness.

10. We Live Here!

ORDINARILY in September we are just like all the other summer people in our Connecticut town. We hasten to can the last of the tomatoes, we cut as many zinnias and marigolds as the house will hold, giving it a decided look of a Funeral Home, we take last walks in the woods, and a last cold swim in the lake; and we load and load and load the car for our trip back to town. The summer is over.

But not every September. Once in seven years it is different. Then the Professor has a year's leave from his teaching and we stay in the country. It is the blessed sabbatical year, the lucky seventh. The University offers to its professors a half-year on full pay or a whole year on half-pay. With complete financial abandon, we take the full year on half, trusting in the Lord to provide, which to date He always has. Let it be said at once that the University does not expect its professors on sabbatical leave simply to loaf! Most of them come up with a book, or another research problem answered, or a course of reading accomplished. My Professor can be counted on for a book.

When the first sabbatical bat loomed ahead of us we thought seriously about what we should do with the time. Southern France, maybe, soft days on the Riviera, a chance for the boys to learn French (not to mention their mother), no worry about the weather, and living cheap enough to avoid other worries. Or maybe Mexico, on the high plain around Mexico City, Cuernavaca, a little touch of Spanish, and frijoles for breakfast. We bought guide books and studied maps. The Professor loves maps. But in spite of them, we could not decide on the particular foreign spot to spend our precious winter in. It was I, for once, who had the inspiration. "Look," I said, "we've always wanted to spend a winter in Connecticut. We hate so to go back to town in the fall. Why isn't this the time? There'll be no traveling, the boys are too small to go to school, we can really learn about the weather, and we'll be Natives. Let's do it."

And we did. A modest hot-air furnace was installed, with a great square register in the living room, and the promise, amply fulfilled, of hot heads and cold feet. We rented our house in town. We had no electricity in those days, but there were plenty of big Rochester lamps with round wicks that held more than a quart of kerosene. We hired an elderly Mary O'Shea (this was before Martha's time) who in her heyday had been cook for the rich (and did not let us forget it) to "do" for us at wages which, although low, were beyond our means. We bought snow tires for the car, and storm windows to protect the north and west sides of the house. We ordered winter clothes from the mail-order catalogue—country winter clothes. And we were ready.

September that year was like no other September. It was not even like the sabbatical Septembers that have followed it. For now we know what it will be like, and we know we shall love it. But that first September we felt a little like pioneers setting out for Oregon in a covered wagon. Or I did. The Professor had spent his young boyhood on a farm; but I was a city dweller, and so were our boys. The country for us meant June, July, August, and part of September: long days, short nights, warm sun, flowers in the garden, the amenities of summer everywhere. Now we were to try something quite different.

We began to feel it shortly after Labor Day. For then the country boys and girls went back to school. We hadn't thought much about country school in other Septembers. But this year we were particularly conscious of it. If we took a drive in the afternoon, we noticed busloads of young ones being driven home, and smoke came out of the school chimney, and boys played ball in the hard, brown yard. There were bushels of green tomatoes on the vines that year, but we didn't worry about them. In ordinary Septembers we should have picked, wrapped, and stored them against frost on some night we were far away in New York. This year we picked the ripe ones and waited. If the temperature started to skid downwards we shouldn't be in New York. We'd be right here, to take whatever precautions were necessary, from covering the vines with newspapers to stripping them.

Along about the middle of the month it was forty-five

at breakfast time. The Professor said nothing, but by nine o'clock I began to smell a new smell in the house—a warm smell of wood smoke. We had our first furnace fire. And it felt good. The kitchen felt good, too, with heat from the brand-new range that had replaced the foolish bottled-gas stove. We needed heat now. And our old cook kept pots simmering at all hours with soup that tasted better than soup ever had.

It wasn't really winter yet. It wasn't, properly speaking, even fall. But we had fire. We wouldn't be cold in the months to come. There was one touching thing we noticed when winter really hit us and the furnace fire was a daily must. Our house was built around 1795. The living room is lined around the fireplace with horizontal chestnut boards, which measure as much as twenty-seven inches across. As the heat penetrated the old house, such heat as, in its century and a half, it had never known, the boards dried and shrank till the cracks between them were a quarter-inch wide. We plugged them neatly with narrow strips of molding—or rather the Professor did—and they did not shrink much more. But I thought of those old, eighteenth-century boards, cut from trees whose kind has disappeared from this country, experiencing for the first time general heat all over the house and not the local warmth of fireplace or stove. I felt a tenderness for the big cracks. They seemed to say that the boards had a life of their own.

The day the full difference of our first sabbatical September came over me began like any other day. It was cold enough for a fire. The Professor came downstairs before the rest of us in slippers and bathrobe on his way to the cellar, started his furnace, and waited in his rocker by the fireplace for it to catch enough so that he could turn off the draft. Then he came back to bed to get warm for five minutes and presently we all got up. The little boys put on their new country clothes—flannel shirts, long pants, wool socks, stout shoes—and we went downstairs to eat buckwheat cakes and sausage, a breakfast that no city slicker ever could or should endure, but that seems just right for the country. The leaves were still on the trees, although many of them had turned; there were still a few annuals in the garden, and plenty of vegetables—beets, cabbage, carrots, broccoli, Brussels sprouts—all good enough, if somewhat tame.

We spent the morning picking apples, the Professor and I on ladders up in the trees, the little boys choosing the soundest ones from the ground and putting them in the baskets. Our apples are not very good, but they are

usually plentiful. We have them sprayed once, and it is quite easy to eat around the worm holes. The best trees are often the oldest and knottiest. In the meadow back of the house stands a big trunk and one thick branch, probably a former sucker. We took three bushels of Yellow Bellflowers from it that year, an apple that is no longer grown because the fashion has changed to pulpy Delicious. The Yellow Bellflowers blush a little on one side and they are likely to have brown freckles on their cheeks. They are hard, tart, and long keeping. I don't know what more you could want in an apple, but anyway, people don't grow them any more.

Midday dinner was pot roast which had wonderful flavors in it that I have never found in this dish before or since. Mary was secretive about the recipe, but she admitted that she put in a little cinnamon. It was, however, much more than cinnamon; there were undoubtedly onions and maybe sage and of course salt and a few ripe tomatoes and black pepper and—oh, well, it doesn't matter. The gravy was dark brown, the meat was almost too tender to slice, the dumplings were small and round and light.

After dinner it was inevitable that we should take a nap.

At four o'clock or so we put on sweaters and caps and started off for the country store where we do our marketing. The same store is now a member of a chain and displays a variety of produce, including fresh fruits and vegetables, which would do credit to a city super-market. But in those days there were only the same unexciting vegetables we could have taken from our own garden, plus apples of which we had plenty. We did buy butter and lard and candles and nutmeg and paper towels and bacon and a slab of the country cheddar which was locally famous. We passed the time of day with the storekeeper. We were, to our surprise, the only customers. In the summer it was hard to get waited on, even with the storekeeper and his two sons and a nephew. But now there was plenty of time to walk around and look at the shelves and taste a bit of cheese and buy a bag of salted peanuts and talk a little politics (the storekeeper is one of the handful of Democrats like us in a rock-bound Republican town).

The little boys, after earth-shaking indecision, finally selected the particular hard candies they wanted from the case in the corner. I checked over my list once more to see if I had forgotten anything and the Professor lighted a cigarette. He looked around the store. "Business falling off?" he asked, half jesting.

"Why, no, not as I know of," the storekeeper answered. "It's always quieter after the summer people have gone."

After the summer people have gone! I rolled the dear, the delightful words around in my head like precious jewels. After the summer people have gone. I looked at the storekeeper hard to see if there was a hidden smile, a twinkle in his eye; he was quite capable of ribbing us. But he was perfectly serious as he tied red and white string around the cheese and stuffed it in my basket.

I was not so foolish as to believe that we had been accepted as natives of a New England town after a few summers and the beginning of one winter of residence. I

knew my neighbors too well for that. But that was what
he had said. He had distinguished us, our family, the four
of us, from the regular summer people who filled the store
for more than three months, wearing slacks and red bandannas and sandals, instead of the farmers' more sober
garb. We were summer people, of course. That is, we usually were. But not today, not this darkening afternoon in
late September, with russet leaves on the roadside and a
smell of frost in the air and a big pile of pumpkins in the
corner of the store. For this brief moment we were not
summer people but Winter Residents—a cross between
people who lived here and people who sometimes spent
the winter. That was all it amounted to.

Yet I was enormously happy about it. On the way
home in the car I put my arm through the Professor's and
rubbed my cheek against that of the little boy who was
hanging over the back of the seat nearest me. I munched a
handful of peanuts and remembered that the old cook
would have a pot of tea waiting for us, with toasted cheese
and crackers. She loved her tea and was glad we liked
it too. The furnace fire would be sending up a comforting
wave of heat. We would pile our sweaters and jackets in
the hall and go into the living room and light the kerosene
lamps. The little boys would make a block house while the
Professor and I sat down to our tea. Outdoors it would be
nearly dark, but inside there would be a warm yellow
light and pleasant family peace.

Well, it was not quite like that. We got home and the
house was warm enough; the teapot was on the stove and
the cheese crackers were burning up in the oven. We could

smell them the minute we opened the door. Mary was nowhere to be seen. But in a second we heard her—we
heard a long banshee wail and down in the meadow behind the house we could see her white apron flapping.

The Professor and I ran, not before I had snatched the
crackers from the oven, scorching my fingers in the
process. Mary was down there all right, shrieking and
waving her apron as if she were pursued by wolves. It
was not wolves, however, but a half-dozen heifers belong-
ing to our farmer neighbor. They were pastured on our
place, in a field down near the road; or at least they were
supposed to be there. But they had got out, and once out
of her own little fenced-in world there is nothing more
frolicsome than a heifer.

Mary was panting. "In the blessed yard itself they
were," she gasped. "In the flowerbeds, trampling and
pounding and digging up the dirt! And when I chased
them they ran round and round. May the Blessed Virgin
protect us from creatures such as these! I can do naught
with them." And throwing her apron over her head, she
made for the house, the heifers gaily streaming after her.

I wanted to comfort Mary but there was not time. The
Professor was already on a dead run, trying to head them
off from the yard. I ran, too, waving my arms. The leader
missed the gap that led to the lawn and the flowerbeds,
and turned along the stone wall. By this time the Professor had overtaken her and executed a brilliant flank move-
ment by which he leaped the wall and bore down on the
lot of them. I was far enough behind to keep them from
turning back. The yard was safe, but the young lady

cows were not in the least disposed to go back to their tiresome old pasture. They had tasted freedom and liked it no end.

"Keep them from the woods," the Professor shouted with his last breath.

I nodded intelligently, tripped over a root, and fell on my face. "I'm all right," I said, as if the heifers were interested in my health—the Professor certainly wasn't. I had lost a few precious seconds while I was gathering myself into one piece again and the leader, a white-nosed nitwit with a large black spot on one eye which gave her a rakehell appearance, galloped past me. The Professor, in imminent danger of heart failure, made a magnificent spurt and got to the gap that led to the woods just in time to head her off once more. I knew they must be kept from the woods at all costs. Not that it was primeval forest, but there was a good stretch of half-grown white pine, and cows wandering here and there in it are almost impossible to round up. So although I was panting like an old dog on a hot day, wishing I could loll my tongue out as far as the dog could, I still ran—along the fence, down to the end of the field, past the gate where the heifers should have gone in (only they had other ideas), up toward the garden, and down the other side. The Professor must have got his second wind by now and was running like a ten-year-old, but I felt that if I stumbled on another step I would very likely fall dead and the heifers could tramp happily over my prostrate corpse. Three times around the field they galloped; three times around the Professor ran madly, just heading them off from this gap and that; three times I struggled on, my scarf flying behind me, my cap in my hand, my eyes wild.

On the third round the heifers seemed to be getting a little tired, which was just as well, for by now even the Professor was wearing down. They made only a few half-hearted sorties before we got them behind their bars once more. We repaired the tear in the fence through which they had escaped and sank down on the grass to try to breath again. My lungs were sore, my knee was scratched, my fingers ached from the hot pan I had pulled out of the oven. The Professor was pretty short of breath himself. But soon he was able to get up and he held out a hand to me.

"Bushed?" he asked in a tone that showed he really did care about my health after all.

"I was," I said gallantly, "but I am recovering. Living

in the country has made me hardy. Also there is nothing like chasing after a cow to improve your appetite. I'm starving!"

"Me, too. Would you like to run for the house?"

"God forbid," I breathed piously. "I should not like to run."

The Professor laughed and took my arm. We walked, rather slowly, up the hill again to the back door. Then things happened as I knew they would.

Mary had lit the lamps and the little boys were drinking hot cocoa and eating newly toasted crackers and cheese. "Did you get the fearsome creatures?" Mary asked. "Frightened out of my wits I was. Now sit you down, and here's your tea."

She set the tray down on the table by the sofa, on which I had stretched out full length. The Professor handed me a cup and sat in his rocker at the fireplace, stretching his long legs out in front of him with a sigh. Our younger boy, always solicitous, came over and stood beside me. "Did the cows bite you?" he asked.

"Cows don't bite," his brother said sternly. "I'm eating the last two crackers unless you come."

But there were more crackers—Mary was just bringing in another plate of them, an angelic smile on her old face. And the room was warm and the light was softly yellow and I had a down cushion under my head and my mouth full of toasted cheese. Life was quite as peaceful and pleasant as I had dreamed it in the car coming back from the village. I drew a long breath and caught the Professor's eye. We smiled at each other in complete understanding.

"Nice," I said. "Very nice." I took a sip of tea and tried to sound casual. "Did you happen to hear what Mr. Yates said to us in the grocery store?"

The Professor ate another cracker at one bite and said um-hm.

"About the summer people?" I persisted. "He said— in effect he said—that we weren't summer people any more. What do you think of that?"

"Wait till we get snowed in," said the Professor. "We'll see how you talk then."

But I was not worried. I had been distinguished in the grocery store and I had caught a heifer. I felt a glow of modest pride and an unshakable confidence. I was really set for a winter in the country.

11. *The Ordeal of the Leaves*

IT SEEMS to be generally recognized that in October the New England trees go on a color jag and dress themselves madly in scarlet and crimson and yellow and copper, not to mention magenta and purple and puce. Dignified maples which have worn a conservative green since their slight yellowy-pink binge in May throw all caution to the winds and select, on the same branch, every shade from sunshine to blood. Oaks turn rosy red, birches stream with yellow, and the beech, ordinarily a perfectly well-behaved tree, cannot make up its mind whether it prefers saffron, cinnamon, or mauve.

All this is well known and favorably regarded, and I shall not labor it here. On October week ends our family, like every other New England week-ender and a large number of residents who will not admit it out loud, wait breathlessly for The Week when the Colors are at their Finest, and though this is an annually recurring event, it is none the less a miracle and we pay our tribute in admiration and wonder.

But after the leaves turn, inexorably they fall. There is absolutely nothing to be done about this. It is part of nature's pattern, and those deluded persons who think that leaves can either be made to stick on trees or, better still—since they must of course give way to next spring's crop of fat buds—be wafted into the upper air and dissolved into nothingness, are living in a fool's paradise and had better wake up. Wake up and rake leaves, that is.

April, I like to think, is crocuses. Purple, white, striped, and yellow, they are to me the symbol of that capricious month when, for us in New England, spring begins to show her face. But if April is crocuses, October is leaves. First the splendor on the trees, then the wonderful rustle and snap underfoot, then the sweet, delicate first smell of decay and death, and finally, alas, the denouement, the catastrophe in the form of raking and piling and carrying them to the compost heap.

A famous mathematics professor who, with his advanced students, dwells in the upper reaches of numbers, asked on an examination not long ago: Estimate the number of leaves that will fall from the trees this year in the United States. I am told that mathematicians take easily to such questions and that they know tricks which will give them what they feel is a satisfactory answer. But I know there is no answer; there is no number, no number could be imagined, which would correspond to the number of leaves in our yard alone on any October week end, let alone the rest of the country. They are multitude, they are host, they are infinite—and they have to be carted off to the leaf pile in the road!

Every year it is the same. We marvel at the colors. We

scuff through the leaf piles on the roadside. We go back to New York with the last chrysanthemums and a little bunch of wintergreen and partridge berry. And we know full well that next week we shall have to rake the leaves.

Some leaves are good for flowerbeds, I am told. But maple leaves make an air-tight wet blanket and should be thoroughly resolved into their original dust before they can be a happy addition to the perennial border. Our yard is fringed with maples outside and with flowerbeds inside the walls which limit it. Ergo, since the leaves are not good for the beds, we must remove them (the leaves; often I have thought it would be far more advisable to remove the beds).

We have tried various expedients for removing leaves. There is no easy or painless way. But for years the Professor, clad in bluejeans and a blue denim jacket, would kneel before the leaf pile I had just raked from the beds, and making a great circle of his arms as if he were performing some ancient mystic rite, would lift an enormous pile of leaves that would not drip much while he walked them to their last resting place. This was when our sons were small and could not be urged to take a responsible attitude toward leaves. They carried a few now and then in a little wagon or a basket or their pockets or their caps, but mostly they considered leaves a perfect medium to jump in, bury themselves in, and throw at a brother. The Professor and I, being reasonably young and energetic, coped with the leaves.

Now, in my declining years, I do not see how we did it.

Later on, of course, the boys helped. I would rake and rake until my arms ached, and the three males would carry and carry until their backs and legs and necks ached.

At any event, that was the carrying-in-the-arms period. But one day when the Professor's young brother was visiting us, and pitying us for our leaf labor, he suggested the very thing which would lighten the burden—an army cart! Now an army cart is a box on two wheels with a handle. The box is perhaps a yard by a yard and a half, and half a yard deep—a sizable container, in other words. It ought to hold lots of leaves. And on a concrete runway, or any flat surface, it should be a handy tool. The first time we tried it, we packed the leaves in good and tight and were gratified by the decrease in the pile we had taken from the flower bed. But leaves, especially when packed and a little damp, are surprisingly heavy. And our yard is uphill, downhill, and full of bumps. I started to push the cart and it got away from me on a downgrade, ending up at the fence. When I tried to pull it back, to coax it to the gate—it was too big to go through the nearest gate and had to be taken to a wider one at the far side of the yard— I struggled until I felt my ribs parting and could not budge it.

The Professor came, gave a strong, manly pull, and by main strength guided it to the proper exit and onto the leaf pile. He then upended it, puffing and blowing in the process, with the idea of dumping it; but most of the leaves stayed inside, defying the law of gravity. They may have been packed too tight, but my hunch is they were simply behaving in a disagreeable, leafy way. With his hands, the Professor pulled them out of the cart and onto the pile. Then he dragged the cart upright and, walk-ing backwards, pulled it across the road, through the gate, and up the yard to where I was raking. He was breathing hard, and although it was a crisp autumn day his brow was damp with sweat.

"Hm," I said. "What we need, evidently, is a horse."

The Professor looked at me sternly and made no reply. He can be stubborn; I realized I should have said nothing. The boys were away, one in the Air Force, the other at college. There was nobody to rake leaves but me and nobody to carry them but my husband. And we were past our first youth, when we used to spend breathless week ends at our new country place in unrelenting hard labor. No, I should have refrained from comment on the cart. It was evident that it was beyond my powers to guide and command. Any sensible man would have seen that it was beyond his. It may be that there are no sensible men when it comes to demonstrating their physical strength. And besides, the cart cost thirty-four dollars and seventy-five cents and was made to be used. It was, indeed, made for carting. The dictionary is not too helpful. Carting is simply "carrying in a cart," or—and here is certainly an additional thought—"working with a cart." Both those activities perfectly described the Professor for the balance of the morning. He was carrying (leaves) in a cart, and he was working (his brains out) with a cart.

After a while, since I had raked all the leaves from the beds and urged them into piles around the lawn, and since I had a lot of chores to do in the house, I did not stay to watch the procedure. Also I could not bear it. It went something like this: The Professor hauled the cart up the yard to the leaf pile, bent over like a peasant of the Steppes, the handle across his chest. Then he stopped to breathe a few seconds. He then knelt and went through his familiar gesture of spreading his arms in a circle and coming up with a wad of leaves which he packed tightly into the cart. He could have, under the old system, carried one armful at a time; with the cart he was moving a half-dozen armloads. Worthwhile, what? I was not sure, as I watched through the kitchen window. When the cart was full and packed down hard, he drew a long breath and hitched up his denim pants. Then he took off his cap and put it on again, pulled his cotton work gloves tight, and carefully removed a wet leaf that was sticking to his shoe. I recognized in these gestures the fact that he was about to undertake a Herculean task and wanted to put it off as long as possible. He looked around casually, probably to see if I was watching, but I ducked out of sight in time. And with another long breath he tackled the cart.

As carefully as if he were moving a ton of loose eggs, he raised the handle and turned it around. Don't let it start rolling, I urged silently. As if he didn't have the same idea! It was perhaps three hundred feet to the gap, downhill all the way, but not regularly downhill. There is nothing regular about our yard. In addition to the bumps and holes there are concealed rocks that send up sharp corners when you least expect them. They are admirably designed to twist a wheel of a heavy object just enough —but I am getting ahead of my story.

I left the Professor, his heels dug in and making large holes in the lawn, trying to hold the cart back in its impetuous course downhill. In addition to holding it back, he was of course obliged to guide it around the hazards of the course. Here a tree root made an incline to the right; there a flagged path, not too level, offered a rough crossing; at the lily-of-the-valley bed he was in the rough. Nevertheless, by a miracle of strength and luck, he got the cart to the gap, turned it at a right angle, and let it slide across the road to the pile. I was upstairs by now, my face glued to the glass, watching every perilous move. I could see that he had no breath at all, and he wiped his forehead with his sleeve before he began to pull the leaves out of the packed cart. I wondered if I should give advice—should I say don't pack it so tight? Or let's forget the leaves this year. Or let's take the cart—empty—over to the incinerator and burn it up. Or cut down the maples. Or sell the farm and live in the city. Twenty-five years of marriage, how-ever, have taught me a few things although never enough. I decided this was not the time to make any suggestions whatever. I could only, in the time-honored female divi-sion of labor, watch and pray.

During the morning I got a number of indoor chores done, but not as many as I had expected because I could not keep away from the window. Once I put on my coat and mittens and went out to the leaf pile. "I'm going to help you pull," I said firmly. "That thing is too heavy for one person." (It was actually too heavy for ten, but I didn't like to say so.)

"I don't want any help," said the Professor crossly. "I'm getting on all right. And it's much too hard for you. Go on back."

As if to prove that everything was under control, he started off with a full load. Perhaps he went too fast. Per-haps he was too tired. At any rate, the cart bounded off strongly, the Professor dragging back on the handle with no result. And then, when he was halfway down the yard, one of those little corners of a submerged boulder caught the right wheel, the cart swerved, the Professor slid, there was a loud thump, and the cart ended at the fence, upside down and spilling its contents on a bed of lavender iris.

The Professor swore. As soon as he got his breath, that is. I wanted to help—to turn the cart over, to pick up the scattered leaves, to straighten the fence wire, badly bent by its unexpected contact with the irresistible force. But I did none of these things. I simply disappeared, vanished, went back into the house and shut the door. I did not watch the Professor pick up the pieces. There are some calamities which even a wife should not witness.

About half an hour later, I did look out of our bedroom window. The cart was back by the leaf pile, the fence was straight, the leaves had been removed from the iris, and the Professor was down on his knees replanting the rhizomes which the cart had torn up. Here was something I could do! Happily I put on my coat once more and dashed out the side door. "I can do that," I said. He did not even protest.

By noon nearly all the leaves were gone from the south side of the yard. There was still the north side and the grass outside the fence that we call the parking. I had debated all sorts of pleasant things I might do, short of bringing up a team of Percherons and a strong set of harness. I considered cooking for lunch the piece of rationed top round that I had bought for supper. But he would probably be too tired to eat. I thought of taking him out a highball, but the Professor is really not a drinking man, and he would have preferred a cup of coffee. Coffee—that would do it, I decided. I was ordering out the red blanket chest in the upstairs hall, and I hurried to finish folding up a big white cotton blanket-sheet that we had used once or twice on a cold winter night.

I don't know what gave me the Idea. Perhaps it was a stroke of genius, which even I might be subject to, I suppose; more likely it was my Guardian Angel or something I'd read. At any rate I stood with the blanket in my hands while I pondered. Then, with a leap that would have done credit to a much younger woman, I made for the stairs, got down them in three jumps, and without bothering to get my coat, raced out into the yard. The Professor, for the fiftieth time, was patiently pulling the empty cart up the hill to the waiting leaves.

"Look," I panted, "I've got an idea!"

He looked but did not stop. With that cart, either going uphill or down, to stop was dangerous. So I waited till he got the cart on level ground and had stood away from it and wiped his face with a red bandanna.

I spread the sheet on the grass and seized the rake. "Let's try it this way," I said, working fast and talking fast to prevent the argument I was sure was coming. But it did not come. The Professor watched me as I raked a large pile of leaves on the sheet and then picked up the corners, making a big fat bag, and pulled it over my shoulder. It wasn't very heavy—he would be able to carry many more; and many more than he could carry in his arms by the old stagger-and-drip method; not perhaps as

many as the cart would hold, but the likelihood of apoplexy was much less.

The system worked like a charm. I got another sheet. On one of them I busied myself raking leaves while the Professor carried the other to the pile. By the time he came back, I had the first one heaped and ready to carry. I cannot say I enjoyed the work, and I am sure the Professor did not, but compared to the agonies of manipulating the cart, it was pure bliss.

By the time the chore was done and the yard was reasonably clear, the pot of beans I had set in the oven was baked. So we sat down to lunch, rather late, it is true, with a good appetite. We were not too exhausted to eat and we were exhilarated with the consciousness of duty done. The Professor mopped up the last bit of bean gravy with a corner of bread. "That was a very good lunch," he said. I smiled. He smiled back. He is a just as well as an honest man and believes in giving credit where credit is due, so: "If it hadn't been for those sheets," he said, "I don't believe I'd have been alive to eat it."

I have only one thing to add to this saga of the leaves. We did not quite clean up the parking or the road opposite the house. In spite of the monstrous leaf pile, there was a carpet of golden brown behind us as we left to take the New York train. When we came up again in two weeks, the road was as bare as my hand! A great wind had come up and blown the leaves—where, I do not know. I do not know, either, the moral of this. Does it mean that if we left them alone, they would blow away by themselves? I do not really believe it. Yet there is that horrible doubt in the back of my mind every October, when our backs are bent and our arms ache with the burden, however lightened by a sheet, of carrying leaves.

12. Back to the Farm

NOVEMBER is the quiet month. The splash of autumn foliage lies in brown piles along the fence rows. The skeleton trees show their natures even better than when dressed in their particular leaves. You could never mistake the gnarled squareness of the oak or the maple's knotty arms or the elm's fountain. The flowerbeds have been put to sleep under covers of pine branches and corn stalks; the vegetable garden is clean of old stems and its neglected weed corners are nicely frozen. Colors are brown and gray, except for blue shadows on the hills on a clear day and at sunset a last pale red among the oak leaves, reluctant to fall.

If we are week-ending, we love November. There is nothing to do but fetch wood for furnace and fireplace and kitchen range, and walk through the woods or across the Hollow and measure the ice in the pond and sit by the fire. If we are staying for the winter we switch the furnace over to coal, the boys walk down the hill to the school bus every morning, the Professor retreats to his study by the pond, and I mess around with household chores or a bit of writing until it is time to get lunch.

The evenings are even nicer. It is time to begin on books in sets. The Professor started to reread Dickens one evening in November and the twenty fat volumes of our old set lasted him all winter. We pop a little corn or toast some cheese or make coffee. The living room is too warm, especially at head level, but my plants do better than they do in the city steam heat. The open fire, which we do not really need, settles to a silvery red ash.

There is nothing more pleasant than an evening in November.

It was on such an evening that Donald first came to see us. Donald had been a student of the Professor's several years before. There was, of course, nothing unusual about students dropping in. At the Professor's office in town there is a steady stream of them, and a few spill over even up to Connecticut. I remembered Donald vaguely, maybe because he had a habit of calling at our house in New York about a half-hour before dinner; maybe because he looked so little like a college student.

If ever a young man had straw in his hair, it was Donald. He was the hayseed of the old vaudeville skit—hair too long, coat too wrinkled, tie askew, and shoes too yellow. He had, I believe, grown up on a farm in the Middle West somewhere, which made him feel that he and the Professor were brothers. It was not his farm background alone, however, that drew him to the Professor; it was poetry. Donald's own fond dream of himself was as a poet; he had come to sit at the Professor's feet, and although I usually respect the admiration of students for my husband, Donald was almost too moony to be endured.

When Donald drove up to our house in Connecticut that November evening I was, to say the least, surprised. He had not graduated from college. Like many another boy, he had stayed around for two or three terms, not doing very well, and then had faded out. I had not even thought of him for years. But here he was, sitting by our fire in the Professor's favorite chair, which he had bumblingly pre-empted, looking just as seedy and wispy and somehow lost, but eager as could be and full of plans.

This was an idea that merited careful thought, and doubly so from Donald. Nevertheless I was rather impressed by the way he talked. He was straightforward; he did not hesitate to admit past failures. He was as modest as he was frank.

"I didn't get on at college, you remember," he said, in his soft voice. "And after I left I drifted around from one job to another—none of them any good and I wasn't good at them. Can't seem to settle down. But one thing I do know is farming. I was raised on a farm—I guess I told you—and I liked all of it. Even getting up early to milk. Seems like it's not right to sleep too late. For me, anyhow." This last was perhaps a concession to our ways. We stay up till long after midnight and think breakfast at eight-thirty is early. I don't suppose Donald was aware of this, but he doubtless suspected the worst.

He crossed one leg over another and held on to his knee, refusing a cigarette. He did not smoke. "There's nothing about being a farmer that would keep a man from writing,

if he had time, is there?" The Professor nodded silently
and Donald nodded, too, and nursed his knee. "Now your
farm, it's a good place. I've been asking around about it."
Donald was full of surprises; it appeared that he had not
just arrived in town. "This place hasn't been used for a
long time, but the land's still good. Mr. Herbert Benton
—I talked to him the other night—says he's still surprised every year by the amount of hay he takes off these
old fields and no manure or lime on them for goodness
knows how long." Mr. Benton is the father of young Herbert, who plows our garden every spring. The two of
them, sometimes with help from the Professor and the
boys, cut the hay and trim our fences. "It's a nice farm,"
Donald was saying, "and it ought to be worked. I came
to talk to you about working it."

We had had such offers before and were immediately
doubtful. Usually it was an offer to live on the place
rent-free and farm with the aid of machinery and stock
provided by the Professor. Since no prospective farmer
had ever expected to make more than a living for himself
and his family, there would not have been any profit for
us except to keep the fields in shape. We had not accepted
any of these offers. But Donald was still talking.

"Wouldn't want to farm it in a big way. Start little, I
think is best. Buy a couple of cows—I know where I can
get them reasonable and I've got a little money—" Ha!
I thought, he will buy the stock; a refreshing change—
"and a friend of mine up in Massachusetts will give me a
pig and maybe a calf. My friend wants to see me get on.
Of course we might have to fix up the barn a little—put in
a cement floor and some stanchions; but if you'd be will-

ing to buy the materials, I could do the work. Wouldn't cost much."

That was roughly the first chapter of Donald's plan. He restated it a number of times in the next few days without much change; he talked well, though somewhat at length. And the Professor listened gravely and smoked his pipe and consulted Mr. Benton and another neighbor or two (who thought the plan feasible if Donald was willing to put in a lot of hard work) and finally, since the outlay would be small and the possible returns not inconsiderable, we decided it was worth taking a chance.

At the height of his pipe dream, Donald envisaged the future of his farming operations on our place something like this: Every morning he would bring the milk and cream up from the barn and leave it in the kitchen. He would bring eggs, too, for it was easy to keep chickens. The berry bushes he would plant would be bearing in another year and he liked nothing better than to pick berries. There would be plenty of room for a strawberry bed. (He figured, reasonably enough, that we would pay for this produce, at less than the retail rate.) He'd put in a patch of corn for the stock and some alfalfa maybe, in the lower field by the road. He'd get lime from the Government and spread it, probably by hand this first winter, but he knew where he could borrow a plow and tractor; no sense in buying tools before you'd earned the money to pay for them. We could rent a locker in the nearest town and he'd put in some pork for us and probably veal, and eventually a quarter of beef. When things got going good, that would be. He figured there'd be plenty of produce left over from what we should use to make him a nice

little living, and he'd still have time to write in the evenings, especially in winter, when the chores were done. Donald continued to think of himself as a poet.

More than that, if we were in New York and the boys wanted to come up for the week end, he'd take care of them. Make a couple of bunks in the little house down the road he was to occupy, take them skating in the winter or skiing; even go rabbit hunting with them or fishing in the spring. Friday nights when we came up for week ends, he'd have the furnace going and the house nice and warm.

If he had been able to write as well as he talked, Donald would have been not only a poet but a successful novelist.

We did not, I may say, expect all these goodies to drop into our laps right away. But there was nothing impossible about any of them—except the boys coming up for week ends with Donald, which I did not much take to. So the Professor, having passed his word, ordered a number of bags of cement from the local hardware store and the necessary stanchions and other tools, and these articles arrived within a week after Donald first made his appear-

ance, along with whitewash to clean up the milkhouse and sundry other items. The bill came to something like forty dollars. Not much, for fresh cream and strawberries, delivered at your very door.

Donald also found a very old second-hand dump truck which he said would be good to haul wood and so forth and he could maybe use it as he did not have a car. The car he had driven up in that first night had been borrowed from one of his new acquaintances in the neighborhood. The boys heartily approved of the truck and we bought it, too, for the modest sum of thirty-five dollars. We christened it Teddy after an old schoolmate with a large appetite for meat and potatoes; the truck, of course, ate gasoline and oil.

Donald, in the intervals of talking, was himself not idle. In a couple of days a big farm truck drove up with a red cow, a black-and-white cow, and a Jerseyish calf. The two young pigs he had brought in our little truck and had penned them behind his cottage. He put the cows and the calf in the old barn just across the road from him, in a dilapidated horse stall, until the new quarters in the barn up the hill were ready. He squared off the barn floor for the cement, put in his forms and assembled the stanchions that were to be set in when the cement was poured. His coat got shabbier and the hay in his hair was no longer metaphorical. He took the truck off all one day and came back with a half-dozen rather limp-looking raspberry bushes. And then he went to bed with a pain in his back.

An obliging neighbor came over and milked the cows in the evening and Donald struggled out and ministered to them a long time after sunrise. The cement remained in its bags in the barnyard, the forms were empty, the stanchions lay in a pile by the barn door. It began to rain and the Professor himself carried the bags of cement under cover. His face was serious.

Eventually, Donald recovered and went back to work. This time he finished the cement floor, not without some prodding by the Professor, who pointed out rather firmly that time was passing. I no longer expected strawberries every morning, but I did hope for the cream. After he finished the cement floor, Donald went off in the truck just after milking one morning—early milking, too—and did not return till the next morning. He had been looking for berry bushes, he explained, without success. He had the air of a botanist tracking down strange flora in the wilderness. I forebore to point out the tangle of blackberry briar just down the road from his cottage.

There are definite sanitary requirements in Connecticut relative to milking cows in a barn, unless you plan to give the milk to the pigs. Our barn, it appeared, even with the clean new floor, needed more windows, not to mention a coat of whitewash, sterilizing equipment, cooling equipment, and so on. We had a milkhouse with a cement tank which would hold water and a block of ice. But every day there would be milk pails to scald. Donald hinted that perhaps they could be washed in the kitchen, but I refused. Meanwhile, the two cows were milked every day, at somewhat unusual hours, in the old barn, the pigs throve on the milk they received, and Donald should have thrived also, for he had all the rest. I was not disposed to use any of it until it was handled properly.

Donald's back troubled him a good deal in those days. In fact, the day after he had finished the cement floor and set in the stanchions, he was quoted by the obliging neighbor as saying that he was being worked harder than any old-time slave. The Professor's eyebrows went up at this but he forebore to comment. So, with a great effort of will, did I. The next day but one he was able to put part of the whitewash on the milkhouse, but it was an obvious effort. I no longer envisioned morning cream. We'd be lucky to get milk fit to drink.

Donald, by the way, seemed a little put out because we would not drink the milk his cows gave. The Professor patiently explained our foolish ideas about clean milk, but Donald, in spite of his college training and the time he had spent in New York, plainly thought it was all nonsense and a discrimination against him besides. He said indignantly that he always washed his hands before milking. Somehow this did not seem to me adequate compensation for the old barn in which he still kept the cows because he had not finished the milkhouse. Also perhaps because it was nearer his cottage and he thereby avoided a walk up the hill.

Relations between us and Donald became increasingly strained. When he first came, he brought the Professor a pile of poems to read—not very good. He no longer did this, to the Professor's relief I am sure. His back got no better. He had to spend more and more time in bed—preferably in the forepart of the day until about noon. But his back was less troublesome in the evenings and he was able to take the truck and stay out till quite late, even past our bedtime. "Maybe we've been a bad influence on him," I told the Professor. "Taught him to sleep late against his principles."

The Professor merely looked at me. He had just written a check for the hardware store bill, more than sixty dollars by now, and had bought two new tires for the truck. The big barn looked very neat with its cement floor unpolluted by cow droppings; the new stanchions stood strong and tight—no cow's neck had ever touched them. The milkhouse, half whitewashed, presented a startlingly modernistic appearance. One morning, as a protest against this form of interior decoration, I finished the whitewash job. Donald was not up yet. The Professor, coming back from his study at lunchtime, caught me at it.

"What in hell are you doing!" he said rudely.

"Oh, well, it didn't take long and it looked so silly half-done that way. Maybe it will shame him into getting busy."

"Don't ever do anything like that again!" The Professor sounded very angry and very firm. He took the whitewash brush out of my hand—fortunately I had just done the last bit of wall—and threw it with great force out into the barnyard. Then he started down the hill in the direction of Donald's house.

"Hey!" I said. "Lunch is ready. Remember?"

"I'll be back presently," he said over his shoulder. "You go ahead. Don't wait for me."

I picked up the pail of whitewash, thankful that it had not followed the brush into the barnyard, and carried it up to the toolhouse. Then I went in and moved the soup to the back of the stove—split-pea soup with a hambone, the Professor's favorite. I wondered what he was saying to Donald. The kitchen was comfortably warm. The red-and-white checked tablecloth—we always ate lunch in the kitchen—matched the blossom on my geranium. I had picked a bowlful of indestructible Johnny-jump-ups that morning and set them on the window sill. Also there were three bottles of milk in the refrigerator, bought the day before at the grocery in the village. It was lovely to spend the winter in the country, I reflected. What did we need any old Donald for? Let the barn stay empty. It had been empty for years now, since Mr. Thomas had sold us the place. I was getting hungry.

It was, however, after two o'clock when the Professor returned and he looked stern. "You shouldn't have waited," he said as he sat down to his soup. He did not smile; he did not say: "Hm, pea soup!" as any other day he would have done. Donald, I decided, was a pain.

"Did he say anything?" I asked.

The Professor shrugged. "He was just getting in the truck to go to the doctor. Said the truck seat was uncomfortable—jars his spine."

"You—you had a talk with him?"

"Yes, I had a talk with him. He thinks having to get up and milk in the early morning makes his back worse."

I giggled. "Maybe we could do the milking," I said; but the Professor was not amused.

Donald's dream blew up finally a few days later. Mr. Benton came over as we were sitting down to supper. His barn is much nearer Donald's cottage than we are. He sat down companionably in the dining room and took a cup of coffee; he had, of course, finished supper a good hour earlier. We have learned that no countryman will get to the point directly. If you want to borrow a tool for the day, you talk about the weather and the crops for fifteen minutes and then get around to the request you have come about. But this time neighbor Herbert wasted no time on preliminaries. He crossed his legs, took a sip of coffee, and cleared his throat.

I started to say something but the Professor signed me to silence. Mr. Benton said: "Them cows—Donald's cows. Bawling all day. Don't believe he's milked them. You figuring to get the milk?"

"He gives it to the pigs," the Professor explained carefully. "He hasn't got around to milking them in the big barn yet."

Mr. Benton nodded. "Kind of hard on a cow. He wasn't there when I went by just now. Just the cows bawling."

"I'll go down with you," the Professor said, getting up from his unfinished supper. But neighbor Herbert waved him back.

"Sit still," he said. "I'll milk 'em. Won't take long. Maybe we ought to speak to Donald."

"I doubt if any kind of speech would make much impression on him," the Professor said. "But I'll do my share." Mr. Benton nodded again understandingly, drained his cup, and got up, accepting our thanks.

Our younger son said, "That must have been what I heard last night. The cows. I thought I was having a nightmare. It hurts a cow not to be milked, doesn't it?"

"Yes," said his father in a strange voice. "It does. And the cow can't fight back. It can't do anything but wait till the man who is supposed to be taking care of it comes around."

Our son's face was troubled. "Poor old cows," he said. "I expect I could learn to milk. I'd kind of like it. Do you think I could, Daddy?"

I hastily intervened, since the Professor was temporarily speechless. "It's Donald's job," I said. "He must be made to do it."

"It's his back," the boy explained. "He said it hurt so on Saturday he could hardly sit still in the movies. And it was a good picture, too. I guess I forgot to tell you—he had to go up to Massachusetts on business. That's why he wasn't here."

The whole affair was concluded within twenty-four hours. Donald, we learned, had sold his cows. He was not able to do all that work, he explained to the same neighbor who had reported his first remark—and who faithfully reported the second. We demanded too much of a man. And his health was so bad. He was willing to work until he dropped, if that was what we wanted. But his back just wouldn't let him. And he couldn't help feeling that the Professor was not very encouraging to a young writer.

So, instead of strawberries and cream, we got a new floor in the barn and a row of spotless stanchions in which, for a time, the boys played Stocks, fastening each other's head in them. Also the milkhouse was neatly whitewashed and I moved the paint cans and other paraphernalia down to it and fixed up a handy little paint shed. The boys adored the truck and spent every afternoon after school driving it up and down our hill and across the fields, since they were too young to drive on the highway.

November was over by now, not to mention Donald. We did not see him again. It was getting colder, and the pond ice was thick enough to skate on. We settled back, waiting for the first snow.

13. Fire in the Mountains, Run, Boys, Run!

THE most frightening half-hour we ever spent in Connecticut occurred during our first sabbatical winter. It was one of the earliest cold autumn nights. The Professor and I sat reading under the kerosene lamps, the two little boys, then six and four, were properly asleep in their beds upstairs, the house was cozily warm from the wood fire in the furnace.

I must explain that our furnace pipe had been put in with a special gadget to warm the guest room. The furnace was in the cellar under the southwest corner of the living room; the guest room, in the front of the house, opened off the northeast corner of the same room, on a diagonal of more than thirty feet. The furnace pipe went under the living room floor on this diagonal and, coming up into the guest room, entered the wall at a right angle one foot below the ceiling. Where the pipe went into the wall we had built a horizontal brick chimney which joined the main chimney stack about three feet away. The result of this Goldberg fix was the upright pipe in the guest room which gave enough heat to warm the room fairly well.

As I sat under the lamp that particular evening, I was aware of a low humming noise which wasn't the wind. The Professor raised his head and sniffed: "Do you smell something burning?" he asked.

"No, but I heard something!"

We both got up, and he went down cellar. "Seems to be a roaring in the furnace pipe," he said when he came back.

I made the rounds of the back rooms: dining room, kitchen, pantry, woodshed. Everything was in order. Old Mary had gone to bed, but there was no excessive heat or smell of fire in her part of the house. I heard the Professor call my name and I ran. He was in the guest room and I joined him at a dead run.

I shall never forget the sight that met my eyes. Words like incandescent and white-hot had been just words to me, but there it was: the vertical furnace pipe in the guest room, from the floor to the wall where it disappeared, was glowing with a pulsing, evil light, both white and red. It was incandescent. It was white-hot. I could feel the heat from it a yard away.

Pictures began to flash before my eyes—what is meant, I suppose, by the drowning man seeing his life unroll as he goes down for the last time. Only in this case it was the present I saw instead of the past: the boys in their beds upstairs; the stairs, a few steps away, the only access to the upper floor; the cold night outside; the house on fire— I did not see how it could fail to burst into flame from this

glowing monster within its very walls; everything burning to a cinder . . . and so on. These desperate images
consumed no time and I made no sound. I suppose I must
have looked alarmed, but the Professor did not attempt
to reassure me. He was alarmed, too. He rushed past me,
grabbed the fire extinguisher from its place by the stairs,
and dashed down cellar. I wanted to follow and I dared
not; that white-hot length of pipe held me spellbound. I
suppose I expected it to explode or something. But I did
go down cellar after all. The Professor was squirting fire-
extinguisher fluid along the horizontal pipe from the furnace wherever he saw the minutest aperture, a crack,
perhaps a screw-hole. Then he ran to the furnace and
emptied the rest of the fire extinguisher on the furnace fire
itself.

For the next half-hour or so we stood by the pipe in the
guest room and watched it. I think I held the Professor's
hand. We did not say a word. The roaring in the cellar
had died down. The incandescence of the guest-room pipe
was fading to a dull red glow. It was only red-hot now.
The man who had put in the furnace for us and had suggested the long pipe—insisting, incidentally, on the horizontal brick chimney which we thought very costly—
had put the pipe through a perforated metal sleeve, both
at the floor and the wall above. After the pipe had cooled
down a little more I felt the sleeve. It was cold!

"Those holes—the perforations," I said. "They must
have kept the floor from catching on fire!"

The Professor nodded and swallowed hard. I felt my
eyes watering. Now that it was all over and the house
was not going to burn down over our heads, I had to cry.

My husband smiled at me and patted my shoulder. "I'd better go down and look at the furnace," he said. "Don't want it to go out all the way."

That experience of having potential, even probable fire right in the house with me, naked and terrible, must have taken ten years off my life. If I die at seventy instead of eighty, I shall know why. Ever since then I have had a wholesome respect for fire—even a spark on the rug from the fireplace is more to me than just a little burned spot. I remember that night.

It was on a spring week end that we had our taste of fire outdoors. We had been burning brush in the newly built incinerator. From the dining-room window where we were eating lunch, my mother said: "Is your fire still burning?" "I imagine it's out by now," the Professor said calmly. "No, it isn't," my mother cried, "it's in the orchard!"

We carried pails of water, we beat the grass with wet brooms, we ran, we panted, we were exhausted to the point of unconsciousness, and after what seemed hours we had the nasty, racing edge of flame under control. About half the orchard grass was black and burnt. But no apple trees had caught and the fire had not spread to the woods above the orchard. My mother, who could not run and should not have carried water, although she did, was pale as a ghost. The Professor lay down on his back on the ground and tried to breathe. I had long since given up breathing. That very afternoon we drove to the hardware store and bought a so-called Indian Pump which is supposed to cope with brush and grass fires. I hope we never have to use it.

As a result of this experience, however, the Professor now saves the brush that is cut all summer long and makes a great pile in the meadow opposite the house. With a permit from the Fire Warden, he waits for a wet day in the late summer to burn it. If it is raining when we get up, and the brush pile is due to be burnt, he can hardly wait.

I don't like fire much, but the Professor really enjoys his brush fire. Martha and I must come out to see the first blaze. Since it is raining, we wear old coats and battered hats. I remember, the last time we watched the brush fire, looking from Martha to the doctor, who was staying with us, and breaking down into helpless laughter. Martha was wearing a felt hat of mine that must have been cast off by Mrs. Noah after the Ark grounded. (I am sure her first purchase was a new hat.) The doctor had an old sweater of the Professor's over her head, tied by the sleeves under her chin. "You look so funny," I said, wiping my eyes. "And how do you think you look in that hat?" the Professor asked me. It was true. My hat was the one Mrs. Noah had discarded before she got rid of Martha's.

We get wet watching the brush fire, but the Professor would be indignant if we proposed looking at it through the front windows—and anyway, getting wet, if you have old clothes on, is fun. The three men poke the fire with long poles or with pitchforks. The Professor gets beautifully red in the face and he and his sons are black from the ashes that blow everywhere. He has a glint in his eye that only a good bonfire can evoke. He really ought to be a member of the Volunteer Fire Department, except that he is a year-round resident of the town only once in seven years.

We had an opportunity, however, on one of those winter days, to see the fire department in action. It was very exciting. We were in the grocery store one Saturday morning when the fire bell began to clang. The firehouse is just across the road. The grocery man's eldest son, the butcher, the garage man, the contractor all began to run toward the firehouse. The town had recently bought a magnificent new fire truck—costing, so the gossips said, seven thousand dollars—and when the firehouse doors were flung wide, there was the truck in all its beauty of scarlet paint and shining chrome.

My boys were jumping up and down in their excitement and I felt like joining them; the old residents, however, seemed to be taking it calmly. Nobody was sure where the fire was except, of course, the firemen, and they weren't taking time to tell. "Let's follow them," I said.

The Professor nodded, and as soon as the red truck had moved slowly out of the firehouse and started up the hill we jumped in the car and began the ascent also. The hill, I may say, from the village is long and rather steep. In the days of our Model-T Ford we often had to let her stop and cool off halfway up. We were not the only car in the line that formed behind the red fire truck, or even the first one. It was a longish procession and as it moved majestically up the hill, with the fire truck setting the pace, I looked at the speedometer. It registered a good, round eighteen miles an hour!

Nevertheless, we went on, in low gear, over the hill, around a couple of curves that slowed the truck down a little, and to another part of town—the prettiest part in fact—with a street of white clapboard New England houses and a church with a tall, pointed steeple. It was too bad, I thought, if one of these fine houses was afire. And at the speed we were making, I feared they would be collecting the insurance by the time we arrived.

I need not have worried. The fire was in the town dump, in a little patch of woods downhill and behind the schoolhouse. When we got there it was sending up a dull, acrid smoke. There were no flames. The fire truck stopped with a flourish, the firemen jumped out carrying their hose and attached it to a handy faucet. Everybody in town was out watching the fire, and it was a very sociable occasion, with the children playing tag and the grownups passing the time of day and exchanging the news. Long after the fire was out, we stood around gossiping. The only thing lacking was coffee and doughnuts.

I was not, however, in the least deceived. Fire was a fearsome thing; I knew it. In a dump, well under control, it was all very well, and an excuse for a pleasant chat with friends. But I had seen it in my own house, and I knew its power.

14. Some of My Best Friends Are Friends

WE had just finished the last bit of pumpkin pie at Thanksgiving dinner and we were drinking coffee in the usual state of postprandial stupefaction peculiar to that American feast. The Professor passed his cup for a refill and yawned slightly. "Let's all take a nap," he said, "and go to the movies after, to the early show." He looked around at his family in simple pleasure at the thought.

"Square dance at the Town Hall tonight, Dad," his elder son reminded him. "And we're going skating this afternoon."

The Professor, disappointed, looked at me. "You and I could do it," he said.

"You forgot—we're asked to cocktails and a supper party at the Joneses. Five o'clock—I told you." This last is the stock remark of all wives to all husbands who can't remember engagements; perhaps all husbands.

"Supper!" cries the Professor, sounding like a wounded animal in a trap. "I'll never eat again—not this day anyhow. And for God's sake, why the Joneses? You don't like their parties, I don't, nobody in town likes them. Why do they have the presumption to give parties? Why do they assume that anybody wants to see them? Why don't they go live in a cave? Why, if they persist in not living in a cave, do they have the effrontery to ask us to their parties? I'm not going!"

"Very well," I say. "You're not going. Although I wish you had bled this way when I asked you if you would go and you told me yes and I told the Joneses yes, instead of this late when they are expecting us." I get up with dignity and begin to remove the dessert plates.

"Sit down," says the Professor in a louder voice than necessary. I do not say that I am not deaf; neither do I sit down, I wait with a plate in each hand. "Don't look so pained. You know you don't want to go!"

"I know nothing of the kind. I don't say the Joneses are my favorite people, but I like them quite well and lots of people I like even more will be there. But it's all right— I'll call them and say you have a headache. You probably would have if you went."

This calm acquiescence infuriates the Professor still more. Practically all wives irritate their husbands in this way from time to time, but it is a nasty trick anyway. He gets up, throws down his napkin, makes a remark consisting of one short word, and strides out of the room. I finish clearing the table and the boys help me with the dishes, while we talk pleasantly and do not refer to their father and my husband. When I come back to the living room the

Professor is not there. I go upstairs and he is sound asleep on the couch in the hall. He is, it seems, enjoying his nap.

I wash my face, brush my hair, and go back downstairs. It is the winter we are reading Dickens and I am halfway through Bleak House. The boys have left to skate. The house is quiet, warm, peaceful. There are no persons around who shout, who are unreasonable, who make life difficult. I decide to read for a while—I am not sleepy. It is four-thirty.

Toward five o'clock I hear the alarm go off upstairs, and in a minute or two the bed creaks, there are footsteps, and the bathroom door closes. I continue to read. At about five-fifteen I hear footsteps on the stairs, and the Professor, his face washed, his eyes bright, wearing a clean shirt and his best tie, appears on the bottom landing.

"Aren't you ready?" he asks in the voice of the well-bred cat who has just swallowed the canary with cream and sugar on it.

"Ready?" I say politely.

He smiles at me sweetly. "Aren't we going to the Joneses?" He sits by me, takes the book out of my hand, and gives me a playful push.

"You are an idiot," I say.

He pushes me again. "Go on, get ready. Don't want to be late. Can't miss a minute of one of those wonderful parties."

I sit back stubbornly. "You don't want to go."

"Sure I do. Go on. I love the Joneses. Can't wait to get there."

"You certainly don't have to go just to please me. I can go by myself or make up an excuse for both of us."

Eventually I go, with considerable reluctance. It is not that I want to be coaxed. It is that the Professor's earlier, extravagant remarks have taken the zest out of the party for me. Now this has happened many times before. The Professor, on hearing—what he has been told and conveniently forgotten—that certain guests are coming to us, or that we are scheduled to go certain places, throws just this kind of fit. I throw plenty of fits of my own, but they are different. I can never become accustomed to this variety. Nor to the sequel, which follows as the night the day.

We arrive at the Joneses. Mrs. Jones, whose red hair is always too well dressed, throws her arms around the Professor, cries: "I'm so glad you could come!" and kisses him on both cheeks. What does the Professor do? Does he draw back with distaste or submit with quiet dignity or simply turn and run? By no means. He embraces Mrs. Jones with an ardor that seems even to surpass her own, walks into the house with his arm around her waist, laughs, makes a joke—is, in short, the picture of a man who has been looking forward to this engagement for a long while and is about to have a wonderful time. This goes on all evening. If he is not the life of the party, the Professor, in a quiet way, is pretty close to it. I am enjoying myself well enough, but every time I look in his direction he is surrounded by a laughing group, or deep in conversation with one or two, or making drinks, usually for somebody else, or cutting a large piece of cheese, usually for himself. One of the women says: "Your husband is such *fun!*" I do not even say uh-huh. It is true.

At midnight I go into the next room where he is, as

usual, the center of a group, and raise my eyebrows while
pointing to my watch, the time-honored gesture of wives
who think it is time to go home. "Getting late?" he says,
holding out his hand and pulling me to the sofa beside
him. He looks at his watch. "Why, it is! We'd better go."

There is considerable protest but the Professor does not
really mean it. Another hour has gone by before we are in
our car, starting off. The Professor's leave-taking of Mrs.
Jones has been hardly less warm than his greeting. "Wonderful supper, wonderful evening," he tells her. My prot-
estations cannot quite equal his but I try to make them
sound sincere. After all, my attitude toward the Joneses
has not fluctuated; I was rather calm about going in the
first place and I am calm at the thought of going home.

"Light me a cigarette," says the Professor companionably, as he turns out of the Jones driveway to the road. I

hand it to him and remark: "You seem to have enjoyed yourself."

"Oh, sure, it was all right. Didn't you?"

"Why, yes. Yes, I did. Not wildly, but about what I expected."

The Professor looks at me. "Still sore?" he asks.

Now there are several possible answers to this question and as many tones of voice: There is the dignified, frosty Why should I be sore? There is the simple, honest Don't be silly. And if you want to start the fight all over again, there is Well, I think I have a right to be sore! I certainly did not want to start the fight again. I hate fights. So I said, trying to avoid all the gambits indicated above: "No, I'm not sore, but I do find it a little confusing when you hate people in one breath and love them the next."

"I don't hate them—oh, well, I may have said something of the sort, but I didn't mean it. They just bore me. Tonight they bored me less than I expected. As a matter of fact, they didn't bore me. I always have a better time than I think I will. You ought to know that by this time."

It is perfectly true. We have been through arguments like this hundreds of times. I announce that several couples are coming to dine with us. The Professor throws up his hands and says why on earth do I ask all the dull people on one evening; or if the mixture is slightly different, he asks why I inflict people like the A's on nice people like the B's. And anyway he ought to work, but of course that doesn't matter. However, when the evening is over, nineteen times out of twenty he says: "That was fine. A good combination." This is not a tribute to my unusual skill at selecting guests. It is simply that he really likes people, likes to entertain them, likes, within reason, to go to parties, but in advance thinks he is not going to like it. I may say there are exceptions to this: There are people he will not ask and whose invitations he will not accept. But in these cases I am likely to agree with him.

So I say: "I know I ought to realize it, but you're so positive. And you overstate your case—you exaggerate. I just can't get used to that, although I know I should."

"Exaggerate!" The Professor's voice has risen slightly. "You talk about exaggerating—why, you are the biggest exaggerator of all time"—this is, I insist, an exaggeration! —"and you don't even know it. Every story you tell you exaggerate."

"Dramatic effect," I say. "But you don't have to try for dramatic effects on me. At least I wish you would tone them down a little."

"Well, I probably won't."

However, he does not sound angry. And I am not. This is no longer a fight. We are almost home, and it has really, after a most inauspicious beginning, been a good evening. So I say: "You'd better begin to work up another fit, because we're having a buffet supper of our own tomorrow night, which I told you about last week, and only half the guests are your best friends!"

"Why—" the Professor begins and then laughs and I laugh, and he drives the car to a stop in the barn. He pinches my arm as we begin to walk up the lawn to the house.

"I won't have a fit," he says. "I'll have a headache."

15. Budgets!

IT usually happens when, rather late in the month, I am paying the last of the November bills. "This family," I announce with feeling, "spends too much money! And Christmas coming, too. We have simply got to budget our Christmas spending—budget it and Live within the Budget!"

The Professor nods. "All right, I'm willing. You tell me how much I can spend, and I'll spend it and no more."

"I'll tell you how much you can spend, but will that keep you from buying a load of books and charging them at the University bookstore?"

The Professor looks aggrieved. "I may have charged a few books last year, but most of them I—or the boys— would have had to have anyway. It's really an economy to buy them for Christmas."

I am a little bewildered by this kind of bookkeeping, but my own hands are not perfectly clean. I have done some budget-exceeding myself. This year, however, I resolve will be different. It has to be. Look at the check-

book! So I do some fast arithmetic and come up with a
sum for each one of us that represents the ultimate in
Christmas spending. We can spend that much and no
more. Not a penny, not a single penny. Although of course
these days pennies have no fiscal (good word!) value, unless you multiply them by big numbers like a hundred or
a million. And in our family we don't think in millions—
not ordinarily.

I do remember years ago, however, when we did. We
were doing the usual daydreaming of young married
couples. We had just bought our place in Connecticut. All
sorts of repairs were needed—new roof, new foundation,
new chimney (the old square chimney had been taken
out about 1850), and so on. Our finances by no means met
the problem. Perhaps apropos of nothing at all, I asked the
time-honored question: "What would you do if you had
a million dollars?" The Professor puffed at his pipe, looked
at the ceiling, uncrossed his legs and crossed them the other
way, and smiled happily. "Well," he said, "we could get
the roof fixed."

Even without the million, the roof was eventually
fixed. But as each Christmas season approaches I have a
strong yearning for a larger share of the hypothetical for-
tune than I know we shall have. It is fun to buy presents
for people you are fond of. It is easy to buy them if you do
not have to worry about the price. I have not the gift of
taking a piece of old newspaper and a yard of string and
fashioning them into an adorable and useful gift for somebody. Neither has the Professor. I sigh and go back to the
family ledger. Yes, that is absolutely all we can spend this
year, no fooling; and that includes charge accounts, too.

The Professor is all too likely to think that his budget allowance means cash spending and that if you charge an object and don't have to pay for it until January, it doesn't count.

We are in Connecticut for the winter, far from alluring Fifth Avenue shops and expensive specialty stores. We do not have to buy greens at the florist's; we can cut and fashion our own (at this I am fairly good). There are no service employees to remember at the holiday season. We are our own furnace man, ashes remover, front-steps sweeper, garbage collector, and the like. There will surely not be so many appeals for Christmas funds. Best of all, the Professor will not be able to go to the jewelry counter of his favorite department store, and choose for me boxes of earrings and pins and chains in a wonderful buying spree, because the salesgirls are so pleasant and the little objects are so pretty and I thought they'd look nice on you and you ought to have some new stuff and I'm sure I don't see why women make such a fuss about shopping—it doesn't take five minutes. I just say: "I'll take this and this and this and this, and they wrap it up and there you are!"

In January I write a check for the bill.

But that, I remind myself, was another year, not this year when we are living within our Christmas budget. We are, that is, unless we want to spend the balance of the winter in the county poor farm.

Painstakingly I make my Christmas list: so much for my elderly aunts; so much for the two grandmothers; my friend the pediatrician; that part of the Professor's family that we remember; and so on. I try to put them all down, and at the end I add the Professor and the two boys and myself, all neatly budgeted. The list looks rather long. Without looking at my total budget figure, I add it up. Like the cost of living, the index (with the budget figure as the norm) has soared to 194 per cent. Something will have to be done.

I chew the pencil. I certainly don't want any member of the Professor's or my family to die, but no matter which one did it would do the Christmas budget no good. We are not due to inherit—from anybody. The sabbatical half-salary is less than half of the regular yearly stipend; the University bookkeeper deducts from each monthly check the amount of annuity we pay on the basis of the whole salary, not the half. Ho-hum. I go over the list again and cross out a couple of dear friends. I can send them a big box of Christmas greens or something. I may have added wrong—I often do. But no; this time my arithmetic is faultless. Oh, well, who knows? Maybe I'll find some bargains.

This is the rankest self-deception, but I am not going to admit it. Not at the end of November, when I haven't even started Christmas buying. I put the Christmas list away in the desk and forget about it for a few days. Then the Professor says: "How about that Christmas budget? You haven't told me how much I can spend."

I get out my list and tell him; firmly. This much and no more for the boys and for me. He nods gravely and writes the figures down in a little notebook. He is the picture of confidence and responsibility. A man to be trusted. Ha.

On the first of December I put on my hat and coat,

get in the car, and to the Professor's question answer brightly: "I'm going Christmas shopping." He smiles and nods, I wave, he waves back, and I start off down the hill. It is a cold, damp winter morning, with a whisper of snow in the air, and the road is frozen hard. I am on my way to the nearest small city, where there is a real department store and a big Woolworth's. At the department store, perhaps unfortunately, we have a charge account. But my budget list is in my pocket.

I begin by a general reconnoiter. And on the first floor I find exactly what I planned to get for my younger boy for two dollars and seven cents less than the budget called for! This raises my spirits immeasurably. I take it as a favorable omen. My good fairies must be with me.

However, the capricious creatures, having given me this feeling of success, retire to fairyland or wherever they live and let me struggle for the balance of the morning. Nothing else is what I want; if it approaches my desire, it costs too much—a lot too much. By one o'clock, when I ought to be home preparing Father's lunch, I am just getting into the car carrying my one package. Drat Christmas budgets. I wish I had that million. We ought not to have spent it on the roof!

On the way home I pass a small nursery and greenhouse. It is on the left side of the road, so there is no excuse for stopping, but almost without knowing it I find that I have crossed over and am in the driveway. The greenhouse woman is by now a friend— I bought roses from her last fall—and she greets me cheerfully.

"I don't want to buy a thing," I say hastily. "I'm just

looking—for possible Christmas presents, you know." This is a lie, but I hope she won't know it.

On the bench by the door there is a ravishing array of African violets—purple, white, pink, blue. The price is about half what I would pay in town. I'd have more money in town, too, I remind myself.

"Aren't they lovely?" she says. "Why don't you take one for yourself now and get some others for Christmas later? We have lots coming along in the greenhouse."

This is very flattering. She has not seen my Christmas budget list. It would be nice to have a plant. Another plant, I mean. I remember I am very late for lunch. But when I get into the car and start off down the road again, somehow there is an African violet plant full of pink blossoms on the seat beside me. After all, I didn't have a pink one.

All the way home I scold myself for my weak-mindedness. You ought to be ashamed, I tell myself; all this talk about budgets and you go and buy a perfectly unnecessary plant when the house is full of plants. I can call it part of my Christmas present, I tell myself meekly. But you won't, you know; if you suggest such a thing, the other members of the family will just laugh and tell you not to be silly. It only cost a dollar seventy-five, I say, on the defensive by now. That doesn't matter (I am being very stern with myself); it's the principle of the thing. Phooey to principles, I say, trying to bluff it out. But I am both unhappy and conscience-stricken.

Although it is so late, I stop on the way up our hill to say hello to my mother. The Professor is a resourceful man, and if I am not there at lunchtime he will either wait or feed himself, depending on how hungry he is. My mother lives in her own cottage and until her present state of semi-invalidism has been entirely self-sufficient and cheerful. Her spirits are still pretty good, considering that she isn't able to do one-tenth of the things she wants to do. She has a small pension, which gives her a fine feeling of independence.

I stop the car on the hill and walk to her kitchen door. She is eating her lunch—a good-smelling soup and hot muffins. My mother is one of the few people in the world who would bother to make muffins for herself alone; good muffins, too. She sets the table properly, also, and uses a linen napkin. I should be inclined to eat out of the pan.

I take a muffin, butter it, and sit down. "I went Christmas shopping," I say gloomily. "But not much luck. Everything is either hideous or expensive or both."

My mother nods. "That reminds me," she says, getting up.

"What do you want? I'll get it," I say, rising, too. She pays no attention to me and I take another muffin. Presently she comes back with an envelope in her hand.

"Now don't fuss," she tells me, anticipating protest, "but I've saved this. It's for your Christmas and the Professor and the boys. But you'll have to spend it. I can't do it this year. Open it when you get home." She puts the envelope in my hand.

I know that her monthly check is hardly more than enough to buy food and clothes for her, and she doesn't buy many clothes. I undergo a swift inward struggle: Shall I refuse it? Of course not. It was given in love, and

I must take it in the same spirit. But I blink a little and clear my throat. "Thank you very much," I say. "And that reminds *me!*"

I jump up in turn and run to the car and back. "I forgot—I bought you a plant. Isn't it pretty?"

Of course she is delighted. And all the way up the hill and into the house, where the Professor, with no idea of time, is comfortably reading the morning paper, I feel better and happier. That, of course, was why I bought the plant. I didn't know it, true enough. But it was right to buy it, budget or no budget, and I am unqualifiedly glad I did. For once my reproachful second-self has no reply.

The December bills are now in and my small splurge with the plant is forgotten in the general financial chaos. The Christmas budget begins to look much too large. I shall have to send greens—free for the cutting—to the whole world. As I am on the point of suggesting that the family go into voluntary bankruptcy, a royalty check that I have forgotten is payable in December comes in the mail and we are temporarily saved. It looks as though we could pay the bills and have a modest Christmas, too. But it will have to be modest! If any member of this family—including me—is caught exceeding his budget allowance for presents (I am announcing this at breakfast) I will . . . I will . . . I don't know what I will do.

"Relax," says my older son, stuffing himself with his breakfast so as to be in time for the school bus. "I am going to make all my Christmas gifts."

"But you charged those boards at the hardware store," his brother reminds him.

"You can take it out of my allowance," he tells me with some embarrassment. "And don't you tell what I'm making, you stinker!" This last is to his brother, who merely grins. The two of them jump up, dash out of the dining room, and we hear the side door slam behind them. Breakfast in our home is not as restful as it should be. At least until the boys are gone. The Professor, doubtless thinking about what he is going to be writing when he goes to the study, hardly notices that I am pouring him another cup of coffee.

"Did you remember that the Purdys are coming for dinner tonight?" I ask him. He winces slightly. The Purdys are winter residents of our town, they are sweet, good people, but Mr. Purdy is a little too sure of himself for comfort—our comfort, that is. He knows he is right and will not brook argument. The Professor, who likes an argument even better than the next man, is uncomfortable with a person who calmly states an opinion as fact and does not expect to be contradicted. However, we are both fond of Mrs. Purdy and do not actually dislike her husband; besides, they expect to see something of us when we, too, are spending the winter.

On the whole, the Purdy evening goes off happily. The other guests—half-New Yorkers like ourselves, who live near by—are pleasant and easy to talk to. Mr. Purdy expresses himself firmly only three or four times during dinner and nobody pays much attention. Afterwards, however, when we are sitting around the fire drinking coffee, we manage to arouse his sleeping dogmatism. We have been, for some reason, talking about money. Somebody—it may have been Mrs. Wilson, the other woman guest—observes that the only thing she and her husband really quarrel about is money. I agree that for us, too, it has often been a difficult subject.

Mr. Purdy clears his throat. "I see no reason for marital argument on such a subject," he says. "It is perfectly simple; the man manages the family finances and pays the bills. After all, he earns the money—he should certainly decide how it is to be spent."

I do not look at Mrs. Purdy or the Professor. But surprisingly enough, it is Mrs. Purdy who, laughing a little, takes up the challenge. "That," she says, "is one of the things Arnold and I argue most about!"

Mr. Purdy is a smallish man with a round, obstinate chin and round, light eyes. There is something ominous about the frown with which he regards his wife. The Professor and I both begin to speak, anxious to prevent a painful scene, but I manage to get my sentence out first. I, too, laugh. "We've been having difficulties with budgets lately," I say. "Christmas budgets. If anybody has a good recipe for making a budget and sticking to it, I'd like to hear it." I look around the circle, smiling cheerfully. Unwittingly I catch Mr. Purdy's eye. He is not smiling; he has not forgiven his wife and will, I suspect, attend to her later. But at the moment he is willing to help me out.

"There is only one recipe," he says calmly (I cannot reproduce the conviction in his voice). "It is perfectly simple: You decide what money you can spare for Christmas gifts—personally I think there is a good deal of sentimental and unnecessary Christmas giving—and how many persons you are obliged to remember, and you allocate a fixed amount for each person. Then you do not spend more than that amount!"

In the weeks remaining before Christmas, the Professor and I often quoted Mr. Purdy to each other with mock solemnity. The quotation, indeed, grew to be a sort of chant. "You decide what money you can spare," I would sing on a minor note. "And you allocate a fixed amount for each person," he would reply, several tones lower. Then we would both sing in the best harmony we could: "Then you . . . do . . . not spend . . . more . . . than that *amount!*" We really made quite a pretty act out of it. I rather wished Mr. Purdy could hear it but I was not sure he would be amused.

Anyway, the budget suffered increasingly. Try as I would, I could not make my gifts and the amounts I had written down as possible match up. Also I had forgotten a couple of people who, again to quote Mr. Purdy, I was "obliged to remember."

The Professor said casually one morning: "I don't suppose your budget allows for stocking toys. We ought to pick up a few little things at the Five and Ten." Now the boys were far too old for stocking toys, not to mention stockings hung on the mantel. But old traditions persist. We used to stuff their small socks with ten-cent cars and five-cent soldiers and a chocolate bar and a package of gum and fill out with an apple and an orange. These treats could be taken down at dawn, if they liked, but the tree and the proper presents were not to be attacked until breakfast was safely over. Ten-cent cars, however, would not do today. In spite of the Professor's optimism, I knew we couldn't pick up a few little things—and if we did they would no longer cost five and ten. The stocking toys turned out to be things like jack knives (eighty-five cents) and pencil and eraser sets (fifty-nine cents); the total knocked my budget out considerably further.

Then I was getting very suspicious of the Professor with respect to my gift. He had asked that a certain New York bill be given to him unopened. This was a bad sign. And a lot of packages arrived from the city which could only be books. Large packages, too. "You really aren't spending too much, are you?" I asked him. "Of course not," he replied heartily (too heartily). "I can find bargains as well as you," he added. Which was all right except that so far I hadn't found any.

When it came time to wrap packages, I no longer looked at my list (I had neglected to add the cost of wrapping, by the way—no mean item in itself, considering that the Professor thinks red string is ugly, cannot manage cellophane ribbon, and therefore insists on real red ribbon to tie his gifts.) I knew the budget and the expenditures did not begin to match. Maybe it is silly to make a budget—though I assured myself that if I didn't, the results would be calamitous. I knew the Professor was perfectly irresponsible when it came to buying gifts for his family. I feared I was almost as bad. And there were so many items I had forgotten: cards, for instance, and postage for them; wine for Christmas dinner; a new set of lights for the tree; and so on. Ho-hum for the Christmas budget. I resolved to forget the whole thing and enjoy myself. I do love Christmas—fuss, extra work, and all.

On the last day of the year I added up what we had spent, as near as I could remember it, and compared it with my Christmas list. I did not know all that my husband had spent, but I could guess. (His present to me was perfectly lovely, very extravagant, something that I had wanted for years, and I was delighted with it.) Item by item I put it down, wincing at the failure of one column to equal the other. Shuddering, I added it up. It was a good round sum, neatly and exactly three times what I had proposed to spend. So much for budgets at Christmas time.

There is a happy ending to this tale, but I hesitate to report it. It happened to us only once, and might not happen to anyone else at all—although I suspect the hardships of Christmas budgets are fairly common. But immoral or not, here it is: During the first week in January, when I had averted my eyes from the bank balance vis-à-vis the incoming bills, we were sitting at breakfast rather late on Saturday morning when the telephone rang.

"That," said my younger boy with extraordinary prescience, "is your thousand-dollar telephone call." It seems that a certain radio program—before the days of Give-Aways—made a practice of calling somebody at random, and the lucky person would receive a thousand dollars. There may have been more to it, but that is the way I remember it.

Our call was not from the radio program. It was, however, from my literary agent in New York, saying that a short story I had written, sold, and forgotten had been awarded first prize in some contest or other, and she was sending me a check in the mail forthwith! So for that one time the bills were paid, we did not go to the poor farm, and the Christmas budget was tenderly filed away in the wastebasket. The moral of this I leave to a better financial manager than myself—probably Mr. Purdy.

16. Christmas Tree

THE first Christmas we spent in Connecticut the boys were four and six years old. We were expecting old friends—another professor, his wife, and their son, a little older than our boys—to join us for the holiday. But since they would not arrive until Christmas Eve, we were obliged to make our preparations in advance of their coming. We ordered the turkey and brought with it a carload of eatables from town. By now it was hanging up in the playhouse, where the temperature was well below freezing. The plum pudding was steamed and stored away, the mincemeat was ready to be spooned into the crust, there were turnips and onions and potatoes and green beans in the cellar, and the house had been cleaned upstairs and down.

On the twenty-second of December we woke to the prettiest white world imaginable. It had come so quietly that even the children had been caught unaware, but it was their shouts that woke us. "Snow!" they shouted. "Snow for Christmas!" The Professor opened an eye, sniffed the cold air, raised his head so that he could see out the window, and smiled broadly. For once we were glad to get up.

After a hearty breakfast of whole hominy (one of the Professor's favorite foods) and sausage, we put on our overshoes and sweaters and jackets and wool caps and mufflers and mittens, and went out to choose and cut the Christmas tree. We had planned to perform this pleasant task on that morning anyway, but to do it in a fresh snowfall was especially wonderful. We clomped down through the field back of the house, making huge tracks in the fresh snow. The dog and the two kittens followed us, the former with great bounds that sprayed snow all over his long nose; the latter mincingly and shaking a wet paw at every other step. The snow had stopped, but the sky was still softly gray, as though it might snow again. It was cold—perhaps ten degrees below freezing—but excitement kept us warm.

This was a very different matter from going around the corner to the grocer's in the city, where the fir trees were propped up along a rope, and selecting one to carry back to the house. In the first place, this was to be our own tree. There were no firs on our place, and the spruces we had set out a year or so before were still much too small. They would have to do for later Christmases. This time we would take a small white pine, one from a grove at the bottom of the meadow, overlooking the highway. When we got to the pine grove, we stopped to look. Each of the trees was wearing its white gown, its lower branches pressed down into the soft white cover. The snow was perhaps a foot deep and every object under it was rounded and smooth. There was no wind; the silence in the little grove was profound. The Professor looked at his waiting family and held up his hand.

"Listen a minute," he said. "What do you hear?"

The boys listened, holding their breath. The older one spoke in a whisper. "Nothing."

The Professor nodded. He, too, whispered. "That's right. Nothing. Nothing at all. But somebody's been here ahead of us." He pointed to the ground and the boys laughed in delight. The snow was crisscrossed with fairy tracks, of bird, mouse, squirrel, and rabbit. The whole forest had been here ahead of us; yet from a distance the snow looked perfectly smooth. Then the dog ran and slid, the cats shook their paws, the boys shouted, and the spell was broken.

It took a long time to choose a tree. "That one," we would say, and flounder to it, and when we had walked around it we would find that the other side was not so good: it was thin or distorted, it had a long branch or a short branch, the top was crooked. But finally we settled on one which suited us all. It was a little higher than the Professor's head; its branches made a perfect cone; it was just thick enough and just wide enough and the top was not too sparse. The Professor took the ax he had brought and, brushing away the snow at the base of the tree, made a small nick low down on the trunk. He stood up and handed the ax to me. "Now," he said, "Mama will make a chop and then each of you boys, so we can say that we all cut the tree."

I swung the ax rather violently, being inexpert but determined, and handed it to the older boy, who made a better job of it than I had and passed it to his smaller brother. The ax was heavy for him, but he grasped it firmly near the head and made a sizable cut. After that the Professor cut the tree down while boys and dog and cats hopped around in a sort of war dance with snow flying around them. When the pine settled down on its side they were silent a minute. The little boy looked at me with something like sorrow in his eyes. "Does the tree mind?" he asked.

"I don't think it minds," I told him. "I imagine it will like being a Christmas tree, all dressed up with pretty things hanging on it."

He smiled and took my hand. His father handed the ax to me, hoisted the tree to his shoulder, and the procession turned back to the house.

After we had got the pine settled firmly in the corner against the library door, there was the problem of what to decorate it with. I had brought no glass balls or tinsel

baubles from New York. We must make our own decorations, I said. The boys popped corn willingly enough, and although they ate a good deal also, there was a big bowl of fluffy white kernels to string when they had done. There was also a bowl of cranberries and—my only concession to "store-bought" decoration—a pile of small red and white striped candy canes and colored paper, including silver and gold, to make into cornucopias and such. I speedily found that although popcorn looks fairylike and insubstantial, stringing it is no easy task. I had set the boys and their father down with a long double thread and a sharp needle. But little boys cannot manage a needle too well at best, and the Professor broke more popcorn than he put on the string. "I'd better do that," I said at last. "You three take the cranberries."

That, of course, was easier, and fairly soon each of them had a long cranberry string which he carefully hung over the back of a chair. Meanwhile I was suffering with the popcorn, sticking the needle into my finger instead of the kernel, with many times a split kernel and once or twice a broken needle for my pains. But it was done at last, and I had three popcorn strings which I added to the cranberry strings on the chair. The Professor meanwhile had been busy with scissors, paste, and colored paper, and had evolved a slightly inebriated angel to hang to the top branch just under a gold star—also cut from paper— that was only a little lopsided. We wrapped gold and silver paper around walnuts and little apples. We rolled cornucopias and filled them with hard candy. We were amateurs at this sort of work, but when the tree was dressed it looked very nice.

"It doesn't mind a bit," the little boy said, his eyes shining. "It likes it." I knew he was right.

There was then the question of lights. At that time we had no electricity and the house was lighted with kerosene lamps. The Professor showed himself surprisingly firm about candles. "Not in this old house," he said. "Not with these children and the animals."

"We could watch them all the time," I protested. "We always had candles at home when I was a child."

"So did we, and one year the tree caught fire and I remember my father stamping it out and mashing most of the presents piled under it in the process. No, you'd have to have eyes in the back of your head to watch properly. No lights this year."

Since he was seldom so firm and when he was, he meant it, we—even I—did not argue; the boys, indeed, were small enough so that they did not particularly care. Christmas was not yet established with them in the firm tradition it was with me. We had candles on the mantel and the desk, and they would help a lot.

We lit no candles until Christmas morning. On the day before Christmas Eve, when the tree was at last trimmed, we had just time to drive to the station to meet our first guest, my friend the doctor from New York. She, too, was to spend Christmas with us. The train was late, of course; our branch of the railroad is in extremely delicate adjustment to the elements; almost any amount of precipitation will slow up the trains. But she came at last, glad to be in the snowy country, exclaiming at the laden branches of the pines, happy at the crunch of packed snow under her

feet. We, as old hands by now at country living, pretended to take these wonders in our stride, but secretly
they were still as miraculous to us as they were to her.

After supper, and when she had thoroughly admired
the laden tree and been compelled to examine and pass on
each individual decoration, we sat down by the fire with
coffee and Christmas brandy. The boys should have gone
to bed long since, but what is Christmas for if not to break
a rule or two? So, at the Doctor's suggestion, they obliged
with a carol.

I can still see them, although they are young men now,
both sitting in the big wing chair, the fair curly head and the
brown one close together, blue corduroy overalls and
brown, stout shoes scuffed at the toes, and cheeks very
pink from a last scuffle in the snow. They sang in the
high, sweet, piercing voices of children the "Wassail
Song"—"Love and joy come to you, and to you your
wassail, too, and God bless you, and send you a happy
New Year." The six-year-old knew all the verses and his
younger brother came in strongly with the chorus, and we
sat and listened and could not quite drink our coffee, and
finally I sat my cup down and waited for the end:

> *God bless the master of this house,*
> *Likewise the mistress, too;*
> *And all the little children*
> *That round the table go."*

And I looked at the doctor and then at the Professor and
tried to smile and knew that the Master and Mistress of
that house felt blest indeed.

The next day was the twenty-fourth. Sad to say it rained and turned warm, so that by the time the visiting boy arrived with his parents there was less snow than slush. The three lads coasted anyway for a little while until they got so wet that their mothers and the doctor dragged them in bodily to change and get dry. The Christmas tree, in its holiday dress, waited primly for Christmas morning when, after breakfast was over and we had fetched my mother up from her house down the hill, we sat down to attack the huge pile of packages piled under the green branches. It was then that the Professor asked for a slight delay while he arranged something. I had lighted the red candles on the desk and mantel shelf; there were no curtains to draw, so the tapers had to compete with Christmas sun shining in the east windows. The Professor was doing something at the tree and I did not pay much attention to him; I was getting out my pad and pencil to make a note of presents that would require written thanks. Presently he stepped back, a sheepish smile on his face.

"I thought we could be very careful," he said, "and just for today it would be a good idea." He had, of course, snapped candles on a dozen branches, real candles, and each one lighted, giving its light which is not like any other light and better than all the electric bulbs ever invented. I felt as I had when the boys had finished their Christmas carol—proud and humble and a little weepy. But I pulled myself together.

"It's a wonderful idea!" I said. And we settled down to the serious business of giving each other Christmas presents.

When the guests were gone, not to mention most of the snow, and the weather had turned cold again—on the last day of December the thermometer dropped from sixty in the morning to zero at midnight—the little pine tree went into its last phase. We took off what remained of the cornucopias and peppermint canes, but we left the cranberries and popcorn and added bits of suet. Then we set it up in the side yard in a bucket weighted with stones for the birds' Christmas. It stayed green for weeks and had many winged visitors, from the happy chickadees, the Professor's favorite birds, to the brilliant, quarrelsome jays. Once in early spring, when it was still standing in the yard and I had just decorated it afresh with a few barberry branches on which the berries still clung, I saw a sight I shall always remember. There was fresh snow under the tree, very white, and the barberries, in the sun, were very red. As I looked through the window I saw four bluebirds enjoying a bright breakfast. Red, white, and blue—a good ending for our Christmas tree.

17. The Night after Christmas

A COUPLE of years ago we decided to spend the first half of the Christmas holidays in Connecticut and shut up the house and come back to New York on the twenty-sixth. (Our academic holiday is usually about two weeks.) This sounds simpler than it actually is. It meant, for one thing, that the water, which had been turned off on our last week end in November, would have to be turned on again for the holiday trip; the Professor is no man to suffer primitive washing conditions if he can help it. It also meant keeping the car another month in New York, mostly resting quietly in the garage, since none of us likes city driving. It involved loading the car to the top with all the Christmas presents, wrapped and unwrapped, which of course we should have to bring back with us when the country week was over. Finally, when we arrived on Friday evening about eleven o'clock, although our friend the plumber had started a furnace fire which had warmed the house a little, the back bathroom pipes were frozen and the Professor and his older son struggled with lighted candles until three A.M. to get the water running.

However, it was a happy week and the weather was just right. We skated every day—well, the Professor and the boys skated; I found that I had left my skates in New York, which considering my dubious skill at the sport was not too much of a calamity. Still, I rather wished I had brought them along. Our appetites were huge and I was kept busy cooking large meals, even including desserts which in our family are usually superfluous. My younger boy picks half-heartedly at all desserts except fruit and strawberry shortcake. My husband looks at the plate that is set down before him, says "Hm!" with patently false enthusiasm, and begins to talk very fast, ignoring the sweet. When everybody else has finished, he puts big bites into his mouth, for all the world like the little boy who had to eat his spinach before his pie—only in the Professor's case he loves spinach and only tolerates pie.

He refuses what he calls "slippery desserts" which include all puddings and most things with whipped cream—"too easy to eat," he says. Once in a while he enjoys a small piece of apple pie made with fresh new apples or a rather larger piece of mince if it is warm. But set a cut of chocolate cake in front of him, no matter how succulent, or the aforementioned strawberry shortcake dripping with cream, and he begins to slide down in his chair and look helpless and put upon, although uncomplaining, and after a while I take it away and eat it myself, which is very bad for my figure. So desserts are a snare and a delusion. My older boy was once able to do away with a quarter of a cake at a sitting. Now he, too, thinks about his waistline and wants a slimming piece, as I do.

There was only one casualty during the week, and that was the Professor for an afternoon. He licked too many Christmas seals! We spent a couple of hours, each in a separate room, wrapping our packages. Time was when the boys would, after struggling manfully with paper and ribbon, bring the object to me and say: "I can't do it; it slips. You fix it!" But by now they turn out wrappings as good as mine, if not better. The Professor uses a lot of stickers on his, in addition to much ribbon, and after this particular round of wrapping he came out of the guest room where his gifts were hidden looking rather pale. "Think I'll lie down for a few minutes," he said. "I feel a little queer."

"Headache?" I asked sympathetically, for his headaches, though fewer in number than they used to be, are of the migraine type and very unpleasant. "Oh, no," he assured me, "not that. I just feel—sort of upset." He stretched himself on the sofa and closed his eyes and I covered him with a steamer rug. About an hour later he got up, still pale but insisting that he felt better. "I think it was those Christmas seals. Made me sick. What do they put on them?"

"Glue, ipecac, and molasses," said his younger son with almost too much invention, for the Professor got up suddenly and made for the bathroom, not waiting for his son's apologies.

He was all right by suppertime, after a brisk walk in the cold air, but for dessert I gave him cheese, which he loves. He smiled his gratitude. "I think I'll use Scotch tape next year," he said. "Licks itself."

On Tuesday the twenty-third it snowed just enough, a fine cover that turned the world white but did not spoil the skating. Friends came for Christmas dinner, but since they stayed for supper, too, and on into the evening, there was no time until morning to begin dismantling the house for the balance of the winter.

We got up Friday morning to find it was snowing again, not very hard but steadily. I whipped around at great speed, taking down curtains, stripping beds, folding up small rugs and sprinkling moth flakes on big ones. The boys took down the storm windows and closed the tool-house and other outbuildings. It still snowed, and we resolved to get away as early as we could. We were apprehensive about the roads on our drive to town and we had a dinner date, though it was comfortably late—at seven forty-five. Our road was filling up fast, but the Professor telephoned to the First Selectman of our town, and as a result, just as we were finishing lunch, the snow plow lumbered up the hill and dug us out. We washed the last dishes in a rush, loaded the car with the Christmas presents, the remains of the turkey, and a dozen other things, and started down the hill at two-thirty, which allowed us almost five hours for a drive that usually took half of that. Still, with the snow, the going would be slow.

It was certainly slow. The Connecticut roads had been recently swept and at first we made pretty good time. But when we got to the New York line the roads were very bad. The first forty-odd miles of the trip, which we usually make in about an hour, took us two, it was beginning to get dark, and the snow was awfully slippery. It was sticky, too, and we had to get out regularly and scrape off the windshield, as the wipers kept freezing and sliding over a sheet of ice on the glass, which did nothing for visibility.

"It's taking us a long time," I said to the Professor, "but we'll be all right as soon as we get to the parkways." It had been our experience in similar situations that as we approached the city the snow lessened, the roads cleared as if by magic, and we wondered where all that winter weather had gone. The Professor turned around and nodded. Owing to the piles of gear, I was sitting alone in the back seat, the three males in front. The Professor said: "We've got lots of time. In a pinch I suppose we could go directly to Sara's, without dressing. She'd understand."

It was a horrid thought as far as I was concerned. For one thing, I was wearing wool stockings, which are not the thing to wear to a New York dinner party. However, I had been smart enough to put a pair of nylons in the top of my suitcase. The suitcase was under a pile of other stuff somewhere around my feet. I managed to fish it out, extract the nylons, and hold them in my lap. Maybe I ought to change right then, I thought. We certainly weren't getting ahead very fast, and even if we speeded up on the highways going into town, we'd need every minute.

It was rather difficult, under the blanket which covered my knees and without making too much of a fuss, to take off my galoshes, my shoes, and my woolen stockings, and put on the nylons, the shoes, and the galoshes once more. It would have been easier to build a new highway without any snow on it. Once during my contortions the

Professor looked around. I sat back guiltily and pulled the blanket up over my lap. I didn't want him to know what I was doing. He would think it foolish. "All right?" he said. "Are you warm enough?"

"Warm as toast," I said, which was not the truth. The nylons were nowhere near as warm as the woolens. But he was reassured and turned to face the front again, whereupon I fastened the last garter and leaned back with a sigh of relief.

We left Brewster at five-thirty, with three-fifths of our trip still to go, although we believed it to be the easier part. The snow had not lessened. In fact it was snowing harder, and the windshield was a continuous nuisance. Every car we passed going in the opposite direction would throw up a fountain of sticky snow which practically smothered the windshield. The other car was being smothered in the same way by us but that did not help. We had no time for petty spite or small revenge.

Our older boy was driving, but after the car had skidded like a skittish horse a couple of times and despite his experience driving a two-ton truck in the Air Force, he said: "Dad, you want to drive now?" and the Professor took over. I must say I was relieved. My sons drive expertly, but the Professor has been managing a car since the age of fourteen, and I am never worried with him at the wheel.

The last lap of the road before the longed-for parkways led around the Croton Reservoir, a narrow, curving stretch that I thought of with some apprehension. At best it was a slow road. Today—tonight, as it now was—I feared the worst. We struggled toward it steadily, however, sometimes in a line of two or three other cars which we prayed would not stop on a hill, sometimes alone in the deep rut the track had now become. We passed several casualties—cars off the road in a snowbank and covered with a thick white cover, looking as though they would remain where they were until spring. The sight was not reassuring. However, we did not stop, we did not slip, and we came at length to the crossing before the Reservoir road. But where there should have been an open road was instead a high bank of snow fronting us like a barricade. We asked about the road and the man at the gas station on the corner shook his head. "Nobody's been through. Couldn't get through now."

We decided we had better telephone our dinner hostess. Her reply was sympathetic and shocking. The Professor reported it to me: "It's much worse in New York, she says. They don't expect us to make it in time. Biggest snow in years!"

We decided on an alternate route. The drifts got deeper and stickier, the road became a one-way rut. By seven o'clock we were going down a long hill in a white whirling world—although it was not cold, the wind was still high—with snowbanks on either side of us that overtopped the car, leaving us a lane in which we moved forward at a speed of about ten miles an hour. Our immediate destination was Pleasantville—ironical name! What we should do when we got there we had no idea.

At last the inevitable happened. A car loomed ahead of us, stuck behind another car. The only way we could have passed would have been to lift the car over the drifts that pressed us on either side. The Professor got

out; the two boys got out. After floundering around in the
snow for five minutes they climbed back, bringing several
buckets of snow in with them. "Have to back up," they
told me.

We backed for an hour, the distance to the first place we
could turn around being about a mile and a half. We
backed uphill, in the narrow lane, through the high banks.
All three of the men tried it in turn, holding the wheel
with one hand, holding the door open with the other,
leaning out to see the direction, taking in quantities of
snow, and inevitably, sooner or later—mostly sooner—
slipping out of the rut and plunging backward into the
snow bank, sometimes on the right, sometimes on the left.
My sons were mostly silent, suffering through clenched
teeth, but the Professor was almost lyrically profane. At
some of his more picturesque profanity I wanted to laugh,
but I did not. It was no laughing matter.

Out of the night several men emerged, probably gnomes
conjured up by the storm, and helped us pull or push,
whichever we needed at the moment. They stood on the
bumper to lower the front or threw their weight along the
side. It didn't really help much, because fifty feet after

they got us unstuck, we got ourselves stuck again. I may say I took no part in these exertions. There were plenty of men about, and having put on my nylons I was not dressed to flounder up to my waist in snow, as the others were doing. Also I have learned that in a real crisis, when I cannot help, I am better out of the way, invisible. So I leaned back in my corner of the back seat and pretended I was not there.

Suddenly one of the gnomes who were attending us leaned his head in the front window. My three were out pushing or pulling, I forget which. He was a little man, a real gnome, and he spoke in a small high voice. "Will you let me try it?" he said. He opened the door and made ready to climb into the driver's seat. "By all means," I told him. "I'm a good man at the wheel," the gnome continued. "Truckdriver."

He was indeed a good man at the wheel. Or perhaps the road was better or we had by our own efforts pushed up to the top of the hill. At any rate, we kept going backward, we did not swerve into the snowbank, and in five minutes he had whirled into a driveway that was reasonably open, had plunged forward, and we were once more pointed in the direction we wanted to go.

The Professor and the boys ran after us and got wearily into the car. The gnome told us where we might drop him—we were, it seems, going his way; he told us, also, of a garage where we could get one of the chains fixed. It had broken and was clanging brutally against the right rear fender. It was two miles to the garage. We made it in about twenty minutes, which was wonderful time.

We were in a village: there was the garage, opposite was a general store—closed of course—and other buildings were faintly visible in the snowy darkness. On either side of the road we saw a number of large white humps—cars abandoned by their owners and left to sink gradually into the primeval glacier moraine. Unless their owners were still inside, reverting to the Age of the Glaciers with them.

The garage man shook his head when the Professor asked him to mend the chain.

"Been working since eight o'clock this morning," he said. "I'm pooped. Going home for dinner." He turned away and the Professor made no protest. I certainly did not blame the garage man. But he turned back. "Hey," he said, "where you folks going to spend the night?"

I do not know why he chose to play good Samaritan to us. Perhaps because the Professor looked at once polite and pitiful or maybe because he did not argue. At any rate the garage man, foregoing his own dinner, told us to drive the car—turkey, presents, and all—into the garage, directed us to a tavern up the street where we might eat and dry out, and spent the next hour telephoning to people he knew in search of beds for us. It was not that people were inhospitable; this was Christmas week end and they were full-up with family or friends. But when, refreshed with pork chops, we made our way back to the garage, he had left an address for us and had gone home to his dinner at last. It was ten o'clock.

The house he had found to take us in was not far away. We walked through crunchy snow up a little hill and came to a gate where an old man was just finishing the job of shoveling out the walk. He was our host for the night. "You didn't shovel that path just for us?" I asked him.

"Would have had to clean it out some time," he said. "I'll take you in the basement door and you can hang up your wet things right next the furnace. Won't anybody bother them."

We did as we were bid, and went upstairs to meet the old man's old sister. They had two neat rooms for us, each with a double bed. I am sure these were the only bed-rooms—their bedrooms. I think they slept on the sleeping porch or in some other makeshift bed. The old man would not think of taking money for our lodging. (He did, in the morning, accept a modest sum after much urging, as "a present for the sister.") We went to bed at once and slept well. We had had an adventure; we had braved the elements; we had met with human kindness beyond all reasonable expectation. Other travelers were sleeping on the floor of the tavern where we had supped. I do not know why we were more fortunate. Perhaps the garage man thought I was simple-minded—because of the plant!

Yes, I had a plant. I had bought it from a near-by florist a day or so before Christmas. I did not need it but it was beautiful—a begonia covered with pink bloom (of course I have a begonia; I have a number of them). When we left the car in the garage I meekly took the box with the plant in it inside the little office and asked if I might leave it there, where it would not freeze.

"What's in the box?" the garage man inquired, naturally enough.

"A plant," I said in a low voice, hoping nobody else would hear me.

He looked at me pityingly. "Leave it on the counter," he said. "We're closing up for the night."

So the plant, and nothing else but the Professor's briefcase and one suitcase holding our essentials, went with us in the train the next day. In the morning when we woke it had stopped snowing, but the radio was blatant and triumphant with the details of the storm—the blocked highways, the abandoned cars, the lost travelers. No chance of driving into the city. No idea when the next train would go in. We left our elderly hosts, the old man assuring us that the blizzard of '88, which he remembered as a boy of fifteen, had been much worse, and sat in the railroad station, along with a number of other would-be travelers, each with his blizzard story.

The ticket seller, a marvel of good temper, was almost constantly on the telephone. "Number 21?" he would say. "Don't just know where it is. Left New York early this morning. Not heard from since. The nine-thirty-five? No, that hasn't arrived yet. Be along in a couple of hours maybe." And so on. We lunched at around one; a train was reported leaving Brewster, up the line; it was coming nearer, it was almost there! Shortly before three it arrived. We got to Grand Central at five o'clock in the afternoon; our two and a half hour trip had taken more than twenty-four.

The old reliable subways were running as if nothing had happened, although the city streets were quiet and empty of traffic. As we turned into West Eleventh Street, a sight met our eyes that was somehow symbolic of the whole twenty-six inch snowfall which had buried New York. The street was lined with mounded cars; it was completely blocked—not by the snow that was piled several feet deep, but by a big red snowplow reaching diagonally from one side to the other. The snowplow was stuck. Good and stuck. We stopped and laughed out loud at the sight. Then we trudged on home through the snow, I tenderly carrying the paper carton in which, wrapped in newspaper, I had placed my Christmas plant.

18. Alone in January

IN ALL the years we had our house in Connecticut, I never spent a night alone there until our last sabbatical. The boys had gone back to college after the holidays; the Professor had been asked to lecture in Illinois, and considering the state of our finances and the fact that he could, on the same trip, visit his mother and brother, he decided somewhat reluctantly to go. He hates to be away from his study in the meadow on those free winters when he does not have to teach in New York. But this time it seemed important. He was to be away four days and three nights.

"Will you mind too much?" he asked. "You could go and stay with somebody in the village."

"Nonsense. I won't mind. I'm a big girl now. Besides, I've got Baby to keep me company."

Baby was a black and white kitten we had adopted from an old lady who lived in our tenant house and who had been taken to the hospital recently for what was to prove her last illness. Mrs. Draper was in her eighties, very fat, almost helpless, but with a mind and will untouched by the infirmities of age. She and her ancient woodchuck of a husband—the last man in the community who could use an adz expertly—had lived in the tenant house for years before we bought the place. When he died she stayed on, sometimes with an unwilling granddaughter to fetch wood and water for her. She would not allow us to put plumbing or electricity in the house. She refused a telephone because in a storm telephones could kill you. When the granddaughters failed her, she lived alone—alone, that is, except for her animals. She always had a couple of dogs and several cats. At the moment she had Pooch, a wheezy beagle (sort of a beagle) who had strayed into her yard one summer morning and remained for life, and Pepper, a floor-mop type with the nastiest disposition God ever gave a dog. The cats were Old Man, a battered yellow tom with half an ear chewed off, and Baby, the kitten.

Mrs. Draper loved them all with great devotion and they returned her love in full. Even Pepper loved her. Baby would walk across her great bosom and settle himself softly on her shoulder, rubbing her cheek with his little white nose. She fed them the same food she ate herself—fat meat, lots of potatoes, broad beans, and cake. They all drank tea with canned milk in it, and during sugar rationing, which Mrs. Draper never understood very well, Pooch suffered a good deal because his dear mistress somehow had lost her sugar coupons and he did like a bit of sugar to his tea.

She should not have lived alone, but it was her home, she and Will had come to it on their honeymoon—he was her second husband, her first having been run over by a train after begetting nine children—and she was determined to live nowhere else. Efforts to make her live with a daughter or a grandchild, or to take her to the County Home where she would have been more comfortable, were met with iron refusal and threats of violence which she was quite capable of carrying out. However, when the Professor stopped in one morning on his regular call to see how she did, the fire was out, the house was cold, and she was lying on the floor next her bed, where she had crawled after a fall the night before. She had not been able to get up. I am sure that the dogs and cats lay beside her during the long night and kept her warm.

The Professor coaxed her and she could not resist him, so she went off to the hospital in a fine new ambulance which she complained of because the bed was hard. We took Pepper, blinded by old age and without a tooth in his mean little head, to the vet to be put out of the way, and Pooch and Old Man were taken over by a relative. That left us with Baby.

Probably because he had been brought up by Mrs. Draper without a harsh word and in perpetual love, Baby was a most gentle and affectionate cat. He loved to climb up and drape himself about your neck, with his front paws over one shoulder, his hind ones over the other, and his tongue stroking your ear. He did not approve of the cold linoleum on the kitchen floor but preferred the chair closest to the fire. He would eat anything, although we no longer fed him potatoes and cake, but his favorite food was cheese, which made him a cat after the Professor's heart.

We were, I am afraid, a little silly about Baby. When the boys came home at Christmas they laughed at us and called him our first grandchild. But it was some years since we had had either cat or dog, and Baby was a winning specimen.

So when I said Baby would keep me company while the Professor was away I spoke only the truth. We finally decided, however, that I should drive the Professor to Pittsfield, the most convenient place for him to get his train west, spend the night with friends there, and come back the next morning.

Baby was perfectly able to take care of himself for one night. He often preferred to stay outdoors rather than in —we had made him a bed in a box high up in the woodhouse, where he could watch for prowling female cats who might be trying to attack him—and if I fed him a good meal before I left and put down plenty of water, he could catch a mouse or wait until the next day well enough. Although we called him a kitten, he was six months old at least, and really ranked as a grown-up cat, albeit inexperienced and uncommonly tender.

He looked forlorn when we drove down the hill, sitting on his haunches in the gateway watching us as if he knew we would be away longer than usual. I felt guilty at leaving him. And after a pleasant evening in Pittsfield and a cheerful breakfast, I set out rather early, partly because the furnace fire would need tending and partly to reassure Baby.

I got home about eleven o'clock and hurried from the car on my way to look at the furnace. From the side of the yard came a black streak at a dead run—Baby, of course, winding himself in and out of my feet, arching his back, waving his tail in the air, and purring like a well-oiled motor. He followed me down the cellar stairs, up again, and up to my bedroom, where I sat down to change my shoes and stockings. At that point he climbed into my lap, rubbed my cheek, put his paws on my shoulders, pressed against me. All the time the loud purr went on. It was difficult to put on stockings with a cat on my lap; I put him down once and told him to wait a minute, but he would not wait; he climbed up again and began his demonstrations of affection once more. As clearly as possible he was saying: "I really thought you were not coming back—I'm so glad to see you—I've been lonely—you were gone so long—I'm fond of you—so glad—so glad—so glad you're back!"

All the rest of the day he kept me in sight and every time I sat down he was in my lap. When I walked anywhere he marched in front of me, tail up and gently curved at the end, still purring. I don't think he stopped purring at all for three or four hours. People who say cats are indifferent don't know cats.

I had lots to do that day—a bit of housecleaning, polishing silver, mending socks, sewing on buttons; in the afternoon I decided to prune the lilac by the side door and went out when the last long golden sunlight was stretching across the yard. It had been a lovely day but the barometer was going down and there was a brisk wind. Also the temperature had dropped from a mildish forty-five to just above freezing. We might have a bit of weather. I hoped it would not snow, because I planned to drive to Pittsfield again the next day but one to meet the

Professor's returning train, and snowy roads can be difficult.

I collected the lilac branches I had lopped off and carried them, the kitten at my heels, out to the incinerator. I may say that not once since I had returned to Baby's riotous welcome had I remembered I was alone. I remembered it now and congratulated myself that I wasn't in the least nervous. We never lock doors in Connecticut. From May to September the doors stay unlocked and unbolted; on sabbatical years they are not fastened the whole sixteen months. We do lock up when we close the house for the winter, although a determined burglar would not have much trouble forcing an entrance. My sister, who lives over the hill several miles, leaves a window unfastened on her side porch with a notice tacked on the sill: "This window is not nailed, so please don't break it." Thus far she has lost nothing except two cans of tomato soup from the pantry shelf and several candle ends from the dining-room chest.

The doors, therefore, were unlocked now. For some reason I thought of this when I walked back from the incinerator. I looked off to the west, through the bare branches of the maples at the back of the yard, and saw that the red-gold disk of the sun was halfway below the edge of the hill on the other side of the Hollow. In a half-hour it would be dark. . . .

I am not really a nervous woman. I'm not afraid of the dark or strangers or queer noises at night. At least I never had been. Yet as I stood in the yard and watched the sun go down, with the cat purring and rubbing against my skirt, I began to feel very strange. Not afraid, really, but strange. So strange that I walked in the back door, just off the kitchen, and to my own amazement bolted it. Then I bolted the west door opposite and quickly proceeded through the house to the side door which I bolted; to the library door, on which I snapped the lock; to the front door which I bolted also. I was now completely shut in. It was time to put on the lights. This was the queerest thing that had ever happened to me—and so sudden! All at once, when I knew it was getting dark, I felt I must lock the doors. I was glad that nobody saw me. But of course if anybody had been there, I should not have done it.

Except for locking the doors, I made no further gestures toward security. I went down to the cellar to shake the furnace, Baby running ahead of me and climbing over the neatly stacked courses of wood. I took down a pint of wax beans from the shelf to warm up for my supper. Baby came upstairs with me, followed me to the kitchen, waited while I made a cup of tea and warmed some milk for him, and sat beside me on the sofa in the living room while I idly picked up a book from the table nearby. It was The Travels of William Bartram, an intrepid eighteenth-century voyager through the wilds of Florida. I am not sure it was a good book for me to read under the circumstances. It was full of rattlesnakes, alligators, unfriendly Indians, rushing rivers, and storms and storms and storms. As I continued reading it in the evening after supper, I was aware all at once that the wind was unusually high. We are used to big winds, mostly from the west and north; this one was north or south by east—sometimes one, sometimes the other. It was no ordinary wind. It whistled and whooped around the house, creaking branches, knocking shutters, rattling doors. At least I hoped it was the wind! It might have been a herd of alligators.

I got up and went to the front windows which face east. The big maples along the road were cracking and grinding as if in their last hour. It would have been frightening to hear under the easiest circumstances: if, for instance, the Professor had been standing by the window with me, or a detachment of United States Cavalry, flags waving, had ridden up the road to the sound of martial music, or six friends had knocked at the door to bear me company—if, in brief, I had not been alone.

I went back and sat down with William Bartram and Baby, but of the two Baby was by far the more comforting. He was washing his face and behind his ears, sensibly ignoring the wind. I resolved to do the same—ignore the wind, I mean. It was difficult. As I turned a page I heard a great gust and whoop. I wondered what would happen if one of the big maples fell on the house. Suddenly the lights flickered! Now, I said, none of this nonsense. We can't have the electricity failing on a night like this. That would be the last straw. (Not a straw, really, but a branch or a whole tree knocking down the wire.) I grasped the book firmly and read on. The lights faded, then got unnaturally bright. Very ominous. I got up and went out to the back pantry, lighting all the lights in each room as I passed through, and took down a couple of kerosene lamps, relics of our old non-electricity days, which we keep filled for emergencies. The kitchen fire was not doing very well. Wind down the chimney, probably. I must look at the furnace; this was no night for the fires to go out as well as the lights.

I set the lamps on tables in the living room with matches nearby and a flashlight. As I did so I caught sight of my face in the mirror over the sofa and after an incredulous instant I burst out laughing! That woman with the round staring eyes was myself. She looked scared to death. I wasn't really. To prove it, I picked up William Bartram once more, met an alligator on the next page without flinching, crossed a rain-swollen river, dodged a wildcat—and the lights went out!

Baby made a remark that I interpreted as "What a nuisance," which was what I felt myself. The kerosene lamps gave a wan yellow light; I wondered how we had endured them all those years. Just as I got both of them burning evenly the electricity came on again. Baby said ur-r-r? I agreed. There was no sense in the whole performance, no plan.

I joined William Bartram in the inspection of some delightful wild flowers and saw with him the giant soft-shelled tortoise with an upper beak hooked and sharp like a hawk's bill and with wrinkled, barbed lips, giving the creature "a frightful and disagreeable countenance." The lights went out again, leaving me with the kerosene lamps. I sighed and closed the book. No use trying to read. In a moment of absent-mindedness, I tried the radio. Of course nothing happened. I ate a chocolate peppermint. Baby wanted one but didn't like it. I felt I should get the poor little thing a bit of cheese and wished the cheese weren't out in the dark pantry. The clock struck nine. Evenings in January were pretty long. Seems as though I've been sitting here half a week and it's not nearly time to go to bed. People don't go to bed at nine; not in our family.

There was a knock at the side door. At least that is what it sounded like. I got up and went out into the hall with the flashlight. The door is solid wood so I could not look out. "Who's there?" I said in what I instantly realized was the voice of a quavering woman advertising the fact that she was alone. There was no answer. I cleared my throat. "Is anyone there?" I said firmly. Baby stretched up along the door and remarked that he wanted out. I picked up a tennis racquet standing near by—at least I would not be caught entirely unprotected—and shot the bolt of the door. Baby ran out, I peered out, the wind banged a shutter, the lilac bush bent double. There was, of course, no one about.

Thoroughly ashamed of myself, I opened the door wide, waiting for the kitten to return, and played the flashlight all over the yard. Except for skidding twigs and small branches and dead flower stalks whipping in the wind, there was no sign of life. Baby finished his evening duty, ran after a flying leaf, and came in, talking about the big wind. I shut the door without haste, put out my flashlight, and started for the living room. Then I turned back and pushed the bolt. I was not quite as brave as I was pretending to be. But to prove that I was not completely craven I went to the pantry, cut the kitten and myself a piece of cheese, and heated up a cup of leftover coffee.

By the time these actions were performed and the coffee drunk, it was twenty-five minutes after nine. Time was certainly not flying tonight.

I decided to clean the bathroom store closet. This is a set of built-in shelves on which we put drugs and bandages, towels, boxes of soap, old hats of mine that I think I may wear some time, rolls of brown wrapping paper, wool mittens, and other odds and ends. Ordering it out was a good idea. After I had removed the contents of each shelf, washed the shelf, and restored the contents neatly —not to mention sorting out a pile of junk to throw away —I found it was actually ten minutes after ten. Also I had a pile of stuff that would burn and another pile of empty bottles and metal objects to be taken to the dump.

I put the burnables in the fireplace and watched them burn, adding the contents of the library wastebasket where the Professor puts book catalogues and circulars—what I call "flat mail." When the last ash was black and curling another ten minutes had gone by. In an hour and a half I could go to bed! Baby was already sound asleep, curled into a round black ball on the sofa. When I sat down beside him he opened one eye, purred faintly, and went to sleep again.

I speedily discovered it was not a good idea to sit on the sofa doing nothing. I began to hear noises. Another knock on the door? Creaks on the stairs, particularly the cellar stairs. Thumps that might be—anything; both outdoors and in. It was now raining hard as well as blowing, and the sweep and patter of the rain on the windows made a different set of sounds, no more reassuring. To my horror I remembered that I had not put the car in the barn; it was standing in the road under the maples. That should not be! It was an elderly car and should be protected from wet weather; a branch might snap off and mash it. Why hadn't I put it away? Sheer laziness or inertia or some idea I'd use it later in the day. What are you going to do now? That car has got to be put under cover.

I got up, making my mind as blank as possible, and automatically put on a raincoat, tied my head firmly in a wool scarf, put on my mittens, and got a lantern out of the cellar, lighting it with some difficulty. Then I looked at Baby. He was sleeping peacefully. When I went toward the door he opened one eye again, stretched, yawned, and stepped down to the floor. He walked to the library door with me, but when I opened it and a gust of wet wind blew in, he mewed apologetically and backed away.

"All right," I said. "Stay in. You're right, of course. Nobody would ask a cat to go out in such a night. Do you want to go out, cat?"

Baby said no firmly. In fact he returned to his place on the sofa and put his nose under his paw, his eyes closed. I drew a long breath and stepped out into the darkness.

It was a wild night and no mistake. The lantern flickered ominously. Yet while I was backing the car around and driving it down to the barn I was not really worried. The wind and rain were quite magnificent and I had sense enough to know that no sane person would be prowling around in such weather. On second thought this did not help. I got out of the car and turned out the lights. The barn was black dark. Hastily picking up the lantern, I made for the doors, shut them, and propped a rock against them to keep them from blowing open—they do not fit tight—and began the walk up the yard to the library door. The back door was nearer, but of course that was bolted.

It isn't much of a walk, but that night it seemed very long. It was uphill and the grass was slippery. After ten steps I was soaking wet, buffeted by the wind, beaten by the rain. I walked with my head down, the lantern showing me a feeble three feet ahead. When I got even

with the corner of the house—the farthest corner from the
door I would enter—I am chagrined to say I began to run.

The lantern went out! I should have known it would,
but the resulting darkness was not helpful. It was not
only the weather—though that was frightening enough—
but I felt surrounded, beset, overwhelmed with nameless
terrors. Things lurking behind trees! Things about to jump
out at me or snatch me from behind! I made the door
in a quick sprint, opened it—it always sticks a little—
banged it behind me and snapped the lock. Then I leaned
my head against the door and let myself drip for a minute.

My heart was pounding, I was short of breath. I had never experienced such terror before in my life.

Baby opened two eyes this time and yawned widely.

It was only eleven o'clock but I was in no mood for sitting up any longer. The kerosene lamps gave a miserable light, one of them would soon run out of oil, and I was not going out to the toolhouse to get more. I put it out and picked up the other lamp. "Come on," I said to Baby, "you're going to sleep upstairs tonight." He paid no attention to me, and I decided I did not really mean it. Frightened as I was—as I still was—I was not going to take a kitten to bed with me. I remembered the furnace, so after a last look at it I went upstairs alone with my lamp, shut my bedroom door, pulled down the shade, undressed, and got into bed, just to see how it felt. It felt very funny. The noises upstairs, from creaks to thumps to possible stealthy footsteps, were legion. I decided it was silly to fight this thing unaided; so I took a couple of sleeping pills, wedged a pair of scissors in the latch of the door to make it impossible to open, and resolutely blew out the lamp. The trusty flashlight was under my pillow.

The noises did not stop. There was a sort of crunching noise, like a rat eating through the rafters. I had heard that before; in fact the Professor and I had laughed and grumbled over it. I did not see the humor in it now. He might actually eat his way through into my room. The wind howled, the rain swept against the roof, the house shook and rattled. Yet in all this din I began to separate out a sound that was unmistakably someone—something at my door, a sort of scratching. I listened fearfully. It did not stop. Then, in a lull of the wind and the rain, I heard another sound, this time ur-r-r-r and a distinct, plaintive miow! In the dark I smiled, got up, took the scissors out of the door, and opened it. Baby walked in, saying ur-r-r-r again, and jumped up on the bed. When I had pulled the covers to my chin he walked to my face and tickled it with his whiskers. Then he treaded the quilt a little by my feet, purred loudly, and settled down. It was astonishing how comforting he was. I had time to imagine only a couple of creeping murderers on the stairs before he and the pills put me to sleep.

I woke to a brilliant morning, new-washed, sunny, fresh, and not too cold. It was incredible that I had gone through that nonsense the night before. The first thing I did when I got downstairs was to unlock every door, just to prove how silly I had been. And indeed I had no more terrors. The next day I drove to Pittsfield to meet the Professor.

"How was it?" he asked. "Did you mind being alone?"

"Mercy, no!" I lied. "It was a terrible night and the wind was kind of scary, but beyond that I was perfectly all right. Didn't I have Baby for company?"

19. Sweeter than the Honey . . .

FOR some three hundred feet, the road leading up to our house in the country is lined with venerable maples. One of them is a soft maple, the first to turn in the fall, its leaves scarlet on top, silver below. But the rest of the trees are hard maples, the last to wear their yellow dress in October, the tardiest to leaf out in the spring. It was only natural that, on one of our Connecticut winters, we should think of maple syrup. Our own maple syrup, from our own trees.

I believe I was the one who suggested it first. But I expressed it only as a wandering dream, a hope that I had no thought of realizing. Something like: "Wouldn't it be fun if we could make our own maple syrup this spring!" I had no intention of doing anything about it; after all, we buy a gallon of syrup every year from our farmer neighbor— good syrup, too. But the Professor is not one to dream.

"No reason at all why we shouldn't," he said.

I began to backtrack. "I understand maple sap is more than ninety per cent water."

"We'll boil it out." He sounded wonderfully confident.

"I understand, too, that if you boil it in the house it gets everything scummy—sweet scummy. You have to wash the kitchen walls and curtains and practically the whole house."

The Professor looked skeptical, but he was equal to that, also. "We won't boil it in the house. I'll rig up a fireplace outdoors, and we'll cook it there."

I believe I should divide what happened subsequently into sections: First Phase, Second Phase, Third Phase, and so on. The First Phase consisted of Buying Equipment. It seemed that there was a small metal funnel with a sharp end and a pouring spout. You drove the sharp end into the tree and the sap ran through the funnel, out the pouring spout, and into a shiny new galvanized pail, hung on the tree by a twenty-penny spike. The funnels were called spiles, and the boys and I made a little song about the sap running from the spiles into the pails (Cockney accent). We had to purchase spiles, pails, lots of each, and spikes, too. There was some talk of buying a rack to fit over your shoulder on which to carry two pails, but I reminded the Professor that up overhead in the toolhouse were some ox-yoke patterns that had been there since the American Revolution at least, and he was delighted at the thought and found that they fitted his own shoulders as well as if he had been a Minute Man or perhaps an early American ox.

So in the First Phase the spikes and the spiles were driven into the maples that lined the roadway, the bright new pails were hung on the spikes, and all we had to do was wait for the God of Spring to turn on the sap.

That, of course, led to the Second Phase, the period of Impatient Waiting for the Weather. It turns out that maple sap begins to run with the first mildish days but they must be followed by freezing nights. Thaw in the sun, freeze under the moon—something poetical like that— was the recipe. February that winter was cold almost to the end. The temperature flirted with zero most mornings and did not get up to freezing even under the midday sun. I particularly remember one cold morning because I had to feed and water the horse.

Blackberry, the horse, deserves a phase all to herself. She was a fat black mare, not a saddle horse really, but a friend of ours kept her to ride in the summer and had loaned her to me to ride that fall. I was an inexperienced rider and Blackberry knew it. When I first began to ride her she walked; after a few days she evidently decided that I could stand a trot, so she trotted; and it was only some time later, when her opinion of my horsemanship had advanced sufficiently, that she would consent to a canter or a gallop. I speak of Blackberry's consenting advisedly. If I made a suggestion that she did not favor, like loosening the reins for her to trot, she would turn around and go home. Many of our rides, as a result, consisted of a long walk with me holding the reins tight on Blackberry's stubborn head. When I got tired of walking in one direction I simply loosened the reins, Blackberry tossed her head happily, turned around, and dashed home at a gallop.

It was not always so. There were bright cold days in the fall, after I had become expert enough to enjoy a canter and if Blackberry was feeling gracious, when we had a fine ride together and I began to believe I was a horsewoman. When the snow came, however, I thought I would not ride, we did not want to have the mare winter-shod, so she stayed in the barn, doing nothing. Nothing, that is, but eat. Blackberry had no interest in keeping her waistline down, and lack of exercise did not in the least dampen her enthusiasm for food. She had the appetite of an elephant, and if her meal was not forthcoming when she expected it, she would yell. We could hear her all the way to the house, snorting, neighing, complaining. Feeding the horse, therefore, was something of a chore.

Immediately after breakfast the Professor would go down to the barn, to the din of Blackberry's reproaches, and pitch down about a bale of hay which she would bury her nose in and start crunching like a dozen good boys eating their Wheaties. He would then clean out the stall, as like as not give her more hay—on demand—and meas-ure out her oats, which she guzzled with greedy, dripping lips. Then it would be time to fetch her water. Since we had no water piped to the barn, he walked back to the house, drew two pails of water, and carried them down to her. She was pretty thirsty after all that dry salad, so she would plunge her black nose into a pail, make a long guggle-guggle, and the pail would be empty. Second pail, ditto. Sometimes Blackberry's breakfast ended there. But there were mornings when she was especially thirsty, and after the second pail was drunk, she would squeal sharply, toss her head, paw the floor, and the Professor would meekly go back to the house and carry down two more pails of water. She would rarely drink much of her second helping, but she wailed loudly if she did not get it.

On the occasion when I was obliged to feed and water the mare, the Professor had gone to New York overnight and was expected back on the morning train about noon, much too long for Madame B. to wait for her meal. He had left with some reluctance. "I don't suppose the sap will start in weather like this," he said.

"Not if the books are right," I told him. "It's much too cold."

When I started down to the barn in the morning, the thermometer by the side door registered fourteen below zero. The ground was covered with a couple of inches of snow that had melted slightly under the sun of the day before and was now glare ice. On the way to the barn the first time I slipped and slid about half the distance on my seat. The little boys regarded this as the joke of the season, and since I was not much hurt, I laughed too, and let them help me up, all of us slipping and sliding around in the process. Blackberry did not thank me for the hay, but told me what she would do if she did not get it, and quick. I gave it to her quick. I also shoved her to one side—she didn't care what happened to the rest of her as long as her head was sunk in hay—and cleaned the stall, putting down fresh bedding.

I am not quite so foolish about horses as the Professor is; he loves them with a steady and passionate devotion. But I really enjoyed myself in the cold winter barn that morning, with the sweet hay smell and the strong horse smell, the seed-strewn floor, the thick-scented oats in their bin, the hay mow full, the heavy twelve-by-twelve rafters high overhead, fastened together with long

wooden pins as they had been for a century and a half. I put the measure of oats in the feed box and watched Blackberry drip and gorge for a minute. I was feeling so contented and good that I resolved to go and look at all the sap pails—a purely unnecessary gesture—after I had carried Blackberry her water.

On the way back to the house, uphill over the slippery ice, I was glad that at least when I was carrying two full pails I should be walking down. I was glad, of course, too soon. Carrying two pails of water down a smooth sheet of ice is harder than it looks. I slipped several times but managed to keep my footing. My arms and shoulders ached from the strain of trying to keep the pails level. I took very short steps and urged myself to take it slowly, despite the loud snorts issuing from the barn. Get your own water, you greedy thing, if you can't wait a minute, I told her. Her only reply was another snort. When I set the pails in front of her she thrust her nose down the first one and drank it dry. Then she looked at me strangely, tossed her mane, and drank the other pail dry also. She then looked at me again, a look compounded of defiance and malicious mischief, and said: "Na-a-a-ah!" I could only translate this to mean more water. I fetched it, painfully. Of it, she drank only a cupful.

I was angry when I started back to the house with the empty pails. Perhaps my excess of adrenalin made me careless. At any rate, I slipped, fell, slid, and ended up at the stone wall bordering the yard, smacking my head sharply on a stone as I came to a stop and banging my shin with a force that brought tears to my eyes. I was in a rage by now, mostly at Blackberry, but partly at myself. As a result I set my teeth and grimly made the rounds of the sugar trees, those that bordered the yard, those in the row down the road, those in the meadow by the Professor's study, even the half-dozen we had tapped farther in the woods. It was a silly thing to do, my head ached from hitting the stone, my leg was tender as a complaining tooth, it was icy everywhere and I was in danger of slipping every time I took a step. Nevertheless, with an obstinacy worthy of a better cause, I looked into every pail that hung on a maple tree. All of them, of course, were empty.

I was more than ordinarily glad to see the Professor, therefore, when he returned from town. He listened politely to my tale of Blackberry's devilishness and said it was a shame and she was an old fool. He also listened when I recounted—having recovered from my rage and being now able to see how foolish I had been—how I had made the rounds of the maple trees. He made a soothing sound when I showed him the bump on my head but he was not really interested. Only one thing interested him. "There wasn't any sap, of course," he said.

Suddenly I was angry at Blackberry again; and at the Professor, too. I had been a martyr and got no thanks for it. "No," I said shortly. "No sap." But I silently told myself that there was a sap and I was it.

There was no sap the next day either, or the next. I recovered entirely from my bad temper and was glad I had not let it show. The Professor dug and chopped the snow away from a flat patch in the vegetable garden, and built his outdoor fireplace of bricks from an old chimney. He borrowed the copper-bottomed washboiler over the protests of Mary O'Shea, who invoked the Saints and declared she would never see her dear boiler again. I was inclined to agree with her, but the Professor solemnly promised to return it unharmed.

We were now ready; more than ready, indeed. We were burning with desire for the sap to run. At least the Professor was. And when February was just out, with astonishing suddenness the weather changed. The thermometer climbed, the wind blew softly from the south, the snow began to melt, and along the eaves icicles dripped all day. At night, however, it was cold. Exactly the right setup for the sugar trees to function.

I went with the Professor every morning to inspect the pails—I suppose I should begin to call them sap buckets. And sure enough, they were beginning to fill. I put my finger in and tasted the sap. It was thin as water and faintly sweet, like the echo of sweetness; it tasted like the ghost of spring, a delicate, underground, inhuman flavor that reminded me of the smell I love best—leaves burning in the fall. I might have grown lyrical about the spirit of summer locked up in these two rites—the burning leaves and the running sap—but I refrained. I said instead: "I'm so glad we decided to make syrup. It will taste so much better because we made it ourselves." The Professor nodded and smiled fondly as we walked to the next tree.

There was a good deal of snow on the ground, especially under the maples; and with the warm weather it was wet snow, which meant that both of us were damp to the waist several times a day, since we had to visit each tree to see how the sap was running. Sometimes the bucket would be full and running over. Sometimes it would be only a quarter full and the Professor would be very disappointed. We figured that ten fourteen-quart buckets of sap ought to make about a quart of syrup, but of course we could not carry a pail that was full to the top without spilling a good deal. We therefore needed more than ten. But the maples were very obliging. The Professor poured bucket after bucket into his boiler. He fed his fire from a big pile of apple wood he had picked up in the orchard before the snow came. Even outdoors, apple wood gives out a sweet pungent smell, and the steam from the boiling sap was sweet, too, only with a different sweetness. It smelled, understandably enough, like maple syrup. This, I should have said, was the Third Phase, that of Boiling the Sap and Feeding the Fire.

We did not keep an accurate count, but we must have poured thirty-five buckets of sap at least into the boiler during the days when the trees were giving their sweet juice. We should, I calculated, have more than a half-gallon of our own syrup. I began to dream of pancakes and waffles. Not that we did not have pancakes and waffles a couple of times a week as it was, but this would be different. The apple wood and the watery sap and the deep snow around the trees, and the trees' heavy black bark, and our being in the country for the winter, and even our wet clothes drying over the register would somehow combine to make this a special nectar, not just maple syrup but our own brand.

When the boiling had been going on for a couple of days, maybe more, I tasted the liquid with a spoon. It was thicker, sweeter, definitely syrupy, unmistakably maple. "What do you think?" I said. "Isn't it time to stop?"

The Professor tasted also, and tasted again. I tasted again. "Tell you what," he said, "I'll build up just one more fire, a big one, we'll let it burn this evening, and in the morning we'll call it done. O. K.?"

I was not sure, but I did not press the point. In the light of what happened, I insist I did not press the point. I did not say, firmly and clearly, take the boiler off the fire and let us call the liquid in it our own maple syrup. I am not trying to escape my share of the blame; but I will say I had a few doubts.

The Professor built up his last big fire. We could see it from the living-room window, glowing red in the winter night. We could see the smoke rising from the fire, and steam rising from the boiler. The fire was still red when we went to bed, on one of those winter nights when the stars are big and bright and near. I was aware that the Professor was getting up very early the next morning but I did not stay awake long enough to wonder why. Presently he came back to our room, dressed in his outdoor clothes.

I was really awake by then. "Where have you been?" I asked him. "Is anything wrong?" For I thought he looked strange.

"I went to look at the syrup," he said.

"Yes?" I could feel that something had happened. I made a guess. "Did the boiler tip over?" I had been apprehensive of this from the beginning.

"No. You'll see when you come out."

I hurried to dress, and put on my cap and mittens while he waited. Together we walked to the garden. The fire, of course, was out, the boiler was resting properly on its brick base. Everything looked all right, but I knew it was not. When I got to the boiler I looked in. There was not a half-gallon of syrup at the bottom. There was no liquid of any kind. Instead there was a film of gray ash. I drew my finger along it and touched the finger with my tongue. The Professor had evidently done the same thing. "It tastes sweet," he said sadly. "I shouldn't have built that last fire."

"You couldn't know. I thought it was all right, too," I told him. We did not say any more, but hand in hand we walked back to the house. There were buckwheat cakes for breakfast, but I noticed the Professor did not put any syrup on his. Neither did I. That was Phase Four.

20. The World Well Lost

OUR place in Connecticut is a hundred miles from New York City, but there have been times lately when it seemed as if the region of bungalows and suburban lots had reached even our town. This is partly because driving time has been cut from five hours —when we first made it in a Model-T Ford—to a little over two and a half. It is also partly because our town is the sort of place that guests come to for a week end and instantly resolve to buy a place and spend the balance of their lives in. The population of barbarian intruders from urban areas, not only New York, is growing at an alarming rate; the town has almost got back to the number of inhabitants it had in 1825. Time was when every customer in the local grocery store was, if not a friend and neighbor, at least a familiar face. Now old summer people like us, who have lived in the town for more than a quarter of a century, look around with faintly snobbish disapproval and say to the grocery man, whom we have known since he was a boy of ten, "Who *are* these people?"

On our first sabbatical winter, however, we felt delightfully far away from town. It was long enough ago so that we had no radio. This does not mean that nobody had a radio, but the Professor is a little allergic to new gadgets. I doubt if we get around to television before 1975. We did take a New York paper but it always arrived at our mailbox a day late (the mail carrier could not wait for the morning train), so that the Saturday paper came on Monday and the Sunday one arrived with Monday's on Tuesday morning. This gave us a splendidly irresponsible attitude toward the news. It took us practically back to the Pony Express and we did not mind a bit.

One Friday night in March the Professor's youngest brother came, with his wife, to spend the week end with us. He worked then—and still does—for one of the largest bond houses in Wall Street, and matters of finance were the breath of life to him. He understood them naturally and without a struggle. I have heard that each month as a matter of course he balances his checkbook to the penny, which is far from our own hit-or-miss system, where the Professor announces to me that the bank owes us $10.55 but he is not adding it to the balance because as like as not next month we shall owe the bank $19.86.

The week end with the New York financial guests— my sister-in-law used to be with the same bond house, so even she takes naturally to investment, banking, addition, and such—was unusually pleasant. The weather was good, the food was good, the guests were amiable. On Saturday morning, however, a rather odd thing happened. (At least I thought it a little odd at the time and then promptly forgot it.) Our nearest neighbor phoned me and asked if we had any cash! Now this was a foolish question because we never have any cash; in Connecticut we live entirely on credit and pay our bills by check at the proper time or thereabouts. We had not yet formed the habit of driving once a week to the near-by shopping city, where we would have needed cash for Woolworth's and the A. & P. And the Prohibition law was still on the statute books: our liquor purchases were few, far between, and highly irregular. We did make beer once and the Professor sat by the brew until five o'clock one morning to do something to it at the proper intervals; but when the bottles were subsequently opened, the contents of each one blew up to the ceiling in a cloud of white foam smelling strongly of hops, so we did not repeat that noble experiment.

I explained to the neighbor that we had no cash and no need for any. She seemed greatly disturbed. "You see," she said, "the banks are closed."

"Oh," I replied politely, knowing that banks do close sometimes—probably taking inventory. "I wish I could help you," I added, "but I doubt if I could scrape up more than two or three dollars even if I robbed the piggy bank." She laughed and said she would try somebody else. I might have asked my brother-in-law, who undoubtedly had some cash on him, but it never occurred to me. I'm afraid I did not take the matter seriously. We were living in a world without money in the pocket and getting on well enough, too. If we had cash we would spend it— the Professor and I are both incurably addicted to this. So it was better to get along on credit.

On Saturday afternoon we drove to the grocery store

partly for the ride and partly to get cigars for the men, salted peanuts for the women, and ice-cream cones for the little boys. Of course we charged these articles. The grocery clerk was saying to the woman ahead of me: "We had quite a busy morning—everybody wanted cash!" The woman nodded and said something I did not quite catch about the banks being closed. I wasn't much interested; banks always close on Saturdays at noon, and at that moment my younger boy was jogging my elbow and suggesting that we needed more cheese, then and now his favorite food. So the subject of banks did not rest in my mind more than a fraction of a second. The Professor and our guests were out on the porch crying to me to hurry. I hurried, we got in the car again, and we took a long drive around our town, enjoying the scenery.

Although we have a happy time discussing a wide range of subjects with the Professor's brother and his wife, there is one subject we avoid and that is politics. We do not agree on politics. Period. End of paragraph. We talk therefore about books (they read all the new ones) or dogs (they are the owners of a Newfoundland puppy) or the restoration of antiques (at which my brother-in-law is a talented amateur) or the position of the father and husband in the home (both men consider themselves put upon by their wives) or any of a hundred other subjects, but we leave the State of the Union strictly alone. Nobody mentions political parties, candidates for public office, the spoils system, liberal vs. conservative, or the fact that the country is going to hell on roller skates. As a result, we love each other dearly, we have fun together, and we do not fight.

On Sunday the Professor and his brother laid some flagstones in the walk by the side door. This was a major operation and necessitated all sorts of preparation. First they each had to light a large cigar. Then they had to sit on the side doorstep and case the terrain. The Professor calls this "epistemologizing," but it means little more than putting off a given task indefinitely while you talk about it and anything else that occurs to you. "We mustn't go too fast," the Professor said. "Got to get this laid out just so."

"That's right," said his brother. "Maybe if we sit here long enough, those heavy stones will get lighter."

"Do you think we've found exactly the right sizes?" the Professor asked. They had spent part of Saturday morning walking around from stone wall to stone wall selecting desirable specimens for the walk and drawing them to the side yard in the boys' express wagon.

"Don't begin to doubt the sizes," I said cruelly. "If you do, you may have to get up and walk around a little, and that might be tiring."

"Just like a woman," said my brother-in-law. "Always wanting to hurry."

The Professor nodded and smiled at me pityingly. "She doesn't realize that this is a philosophical concept, a metaphysical exercise."

"And the only exercise you ever want to take," I pointed out, glad of the opening. My sister-in-law laughed and agreed.

They both got up, sadly shaking their heads. "They do not understand us," the Professor said. "Boy, I gather public opinion feels that if we're going to lay a walk we've got to lift some stones."

"I seem to get that feeling, too," said his brother.

They had a lovely morning. The Professor is never so happy as when he is with one or more of his brothers, and they seem to return the sentiment. They carried a stone, panted, laid it down, smoked, considered, walked around it, dug out under it, patted it into place, smoked and considered some more, dug it up again, and so on. The little boys tumbled around their feet, getting in the way, "helping," and running off to some other game when they were bored. By the time we called them to dinner at one-thirty they had laid a sizable length of walk, very neatly, too.

"For such a gabby pair," I said, "you do a pretty good job."

"I think they're wonderful!" my sister-in-law said. The Professor kissed her cheek in gratitude. "Maybe we ought to give you each a tip."

"I'd have to write a check for it," I said, remembering the cash situation. This was considered fairly funny and because everybody felt happy anyway, they all laughed.

By suppertime the walk was finished, the boys had jumped up and down on it, the women had admired it several times—by request—and we settled down in the evening to a game of pinochle. The guests were not leaving until Monday morning. There was nothing much doing downtown, my brother-in-law explained. The depression had been going on for several years and in Wall Street a dozen spears of green grass had been detected in a flourishing state. So he felt he could take a half-day off without serious damage to the country's financial standing.

It was a typical March morning when we got up to drive them to the train: blowy, dark, with spits of rain now and then. "Too bad you have to go back to the city from this beautiful place," said the Professor, putting on the car lights to see his way down the hill.

"And on such a lovely day, too," I added. But secretly I liked the day. I like all days, of whatever kind. I have never been one to complain seriously about the weather.

We were ten minutes early for the train—the Professor is always early for trains—so I stopped in the grocery store to pick up a few odds and ends and thus save a trip to town later in the day. A copy of Monday's New York *Times*, fresh off the early-morning milk train, lay on the counter. The headlines were big and black: ROOSEVELT ORDERS FOUR-DAY BANK HOLIDAY: PUTS EMBARGO ON GOLD. There was also reference to the fact that all banks in New York State and in Illinois had been closed by order of their respective governors on Saturday; even the quickest glance made it clear that the financial district had been in a tizzy all week end.

My first instinct was one of horror at the collapse of national credit, my second was to laugh, my third was to pity my brother-in-law, who had been absent from Wall Street's biggest crisis without knowing anything about it. For a second I thought perhaps I should conceal it from him this short while longer, until he was on the train, but my better nature triumphed. I bought the paper, and took it out to where the others waited in the car.

"No wonder people were looking for cash," I said, and handed the paper to the Professor's brother.

He is a man of great self-restraint, a gentleman, and he is fond of us. So he did not cry out, or curse us for having asked him to a country week end where there was no

news, or utter any reproach whatever. He read the headlines in silence, made as if to hand the paper back to me,
and when I said I had bought it for him, folded it and
tucked it under his arm. At that moment the train whistled.

We saw them off in a hurry and there was no time for
more than good-byes and thanks and come-agains and
such-a-good-times. But I noted, as the train went slowly
past us out of the station that, although my sister-in-law
was sitting by the window and waving to us, her husband
had already opened the paper and was deep in the news.

"Poor fellow," I said to the Professor, "it must be awful
for him to think he didn't know about it. I suppose he'd
have gone back to town right away."

"Um-hm," said the Professor, getting back into the car.
Then he turned and looked at me. "I expect we're pretty
far away from things up here. Do you mind?"

A big drop of rain hit me on the nose as I shut the car
window to keep the March wind out. I settled my skirt
and put on my right mitten. "Not so you'd notice it," I
said. "Do you know—that wind smelled of spring!"

21. Escape to the City

THE big snow of that winter came on St. Valentine's Day. The evening before, our brand-new car had been delivered. In the morning we found the heater needed adjusting, so in a high northeast wind and a considerable snowfall, we drove it back to the garage. When we returned, shortly before lunch, one of the maples in our row fell just behind us as we brought the car to a stop in front of the house. There was less than a foot between the fallen trunk and our new back bumper. It was still snowing hard.

The Professor got out of the car, looked at the tree, looked at me, smiled feebly, and said: "Hm." I said nothing. I merely looked at the tree.

The afternoon was spent, with the help of a couple of neighbors, in sawing the fallen trunk in two and shoving it to one side so that we could put the car down in the barn. There were about six inches of snow and the fall showed no signs of letting up. We were expecting guests for dinner and the Professor telephoned them and said he would meet them at the bottom of the hill, since he felt he knew the vagaries of our road better than anyone. It worked beautifully. The guests, by arrangement, arrived at about the same time, they piled into the new car, the women in long skirts, the men, less optimistic, wearing galoshes and heavy tweeds, and the Professor drove them manfully up the hill without skidding or sliding or stopping even once.

Our sons had supped with my mother in her house down the hill. At about nine o'clock the Professor went down the hill again in the snow to fetch them home—a foolish gesture, since they would vastly have preferred to walk. In those days our road was a narrow one-track lane with deep ditches, sometimes as deep as two feet, on either side. On the way up the new car, plowing through a good foot of snow by now, skidded sharply with its nose pointed toward the deepest part of the ditch. The Professor turned the wheel to right it, it responded, the car plunged too far in the opposite direction, and ended diagonally across the road, refusing, thereafter, to budge.

The guests walked down the hill to their cars through what was by now a regular blizzard. We went to bed. There was nothing to do about the car. Nothing could harm it, unless snow was harmful. Nobody could steal it, even if there was a thief in the whole of Litchfield County out on such a night. The last thing I heard before I went to sleep was the swish of snow on the window. It was a proper storm indeed. The boys thought highly of it, but I was not so sure.

For the next six weeks, while February rolled into March and March was almost ready for April, we lived in a white world. We skied, walked in the crunchy woods, slid down the hill on the boys' sleds, shoveled paths—many, many paths—waited for the snowplow, and watched the road fill up again with drifts an hour after it had dug us out. On several days there was no school —the buses could not get through. We walked to the next farm for the milk and I discovered that to carry five quarts of milk a mile over a snowy road is not easy. My younger boy went with me and we took turns carrying the pail. The Professor and his other offspring were busy with the eternal shoveling out: a path from the door to the gate, a path from the barn to the road, and so on.

There were days when we could get the car up and down the hill, although even with chains it chattered painfully and the new clutch wore out and had to be replaced. On other days we either left the car at the bottom of the hill and pulled the groceries up on a sled, or we left it in the barn and did not go anywhere except on foot. After all, we had shelves full of canned fruit and vegetables in the cellar, besides a bin of potatoes and several barrels of apples, not to mention canned meat of various sorts. We did not suffer for want of food. Beyond carrying the milk, which we did not have to do very often, we suffered no hardship, though one day the box of supplies which the boys were pulling up the hill on a sled fell off and nine of a dozen eggs were broken. And even this cloud had a lining of angel food.

No, there was no hardship. The boys loved the snow. They skied down the hill every morning, left their skis upright in a snowbank while they climbed into the school bus, and skied in the afternoon when they came home. I improved my waistline by shoveling, the Professor worked each morning in his study, heated by a capable sheet-iron stove, the thermometer ranged from thirty down to zero. Sometimes we had a slight thaw, with everything dripping, but in the main we had snow and more snow, snow and ice, snowdrifts, snow forts in the side yard, snow white and even on the other side of the Hollow, the stone walls buried in snow, so that the boys coasted over them all the way down to their grandmother's: in short, we had snow.

Martha had come up to spend the winter with us. She loved the country in the summer, and she was willing to try it the year around. She put food out for the birds, scolding the jays who stole suet from the little birds under her nose and merely scolded her back; she drove her car with new snow tires up and down the road, she buckled on her galoshes when she hung out the wash, and in general was

a happy country dweller—until the big snow came. When she could no longer use her car, she refused to be dependent on us for transportation; and indeed our transportation was erratic enough. We might go or we might not, depending, of course, on the state of the road. And we did not especially care. But Martha was lonely for her friends. So after a month of drifts, she sadly departed for New York. If we wanted her, she said, she would return in the spring. Winter in the country was not for her.

At the end of March the snow was going into its sixth week: the February snow that had come to us as a big white Valentine. I woke up to the usual whirl of white—another snowfall. Our paths, shoveled a couple of days before, were buried again. The shrubs in the yard were bent to the ground by the fresh weight. I knew the road was drifted full. No chance of getting the car out of the barn; have to walk for the milk again. Probably no school, but I couldn't be sure, so I'd have to get up. Hate to get up on a cold morning. Hate to get up in a snowfall. Hate to get up.

I rose, dressed, aroused the other members of the family. The rooms downstairs were warm. Thank Heaven for coal in the furnace; wood would have burned out overnight. There were no phone messages during breakfast about school not being held, so the boys got themselves ready and plowed off down the hill, red cap and blue cap, both white by the time they got to the dip by the barn. The Professor put on his winter outfit from Montgomery Ward, including his sheep-lined coat, and left for the study by the pond. I washed the dishes, made the beds, and whisked a dustcloth here and there without enthusiasm. Three chickadees were feeding at the cocoanut shell filled with fat and seeds that we had hung by the kitchen window. I took heart a little. If a chickadee could take it, I could. And where was my boast that I never minded the weather?

I decided I would go out. I was glad I had bought snow boots from Montgomery Ward. I was glad my friend the baby doctor had given me for Christmas a white knitted cap that made me look like one of her own patients, slightly oversized, but it kept my ears warm. I was glad my other friend, the local doctor's wife, had knitted me white mittens with red roses on them. Thank God for small blessings. Nevertheless, I ought to walk for the milk. The boys would not be home till dark, the Professor was trying to finish a book. Be a brave girl, I told myself. Take up the milk pail and get started.

I was wearing my old riding pants from the days of Blackberry, the stubborn mare, so it was not bad going downhill. I stopped in to see my mother and have her praise me for going for the milk all by myself. "I wish I could go with you," she said wistfully. Her snow-walking days were over. It was all she could do to navigate on level grass. I did not tell her how much I longed not only for company on my walk but for help in carrying the full pail. Instead I minimized the trials ahead of me.

"It isn't so bad," I said. "Fun, really. I don't think it's snowing as hard as it was."

She looked dubiously out the window. "It seems hard to me," she said.

"It's nothing," I replied, "just a little old snow." And I set off.

Down to the main road, around past the cemetery, and

up to neighbor Herbert's was comparatively easy. The main road had been swept, and although a couple of inches had fallen since and it was slippery, I found by walking along the sides I slipped only every third step or so and was never above my knees in snow. When I reached the barnyard I was a little out of breath, but otherwise no damage was done. Nobody was around as I opened the milkhouse door, lifted the top of the cooler, pulled out the full pail, and shut the cooler again. I set the pail down and walked through the swinging door into the big barn, where the cows in their stanchions were placidly chewing their hay. The smell of a cow barn is a wonderful thing on a cold morning, sweet, pungent, milky. A new black kitten wobbled up and sniffed at my shoe. I picked it up and let it lick my chin. A calf in the pen at the other end of the barn bawled and one of the big bay horses opposite him answered with a staccato whinny. The cows said nothing; they were too busy chewing. I put the kitten down and went back to my milk pail. It was all very well to admire rural sights and smells, but I had work to do.

Snow was still pelting my face when I lugged the milk pail out to the road again. Weighted by five quarts of milk, I seemed to sink deeper at every step than I had with the empty pail. I tried carrying the pail in my right hand till my arm was about to part company with my shoulder. Then I shifted to the left hand and waited till my fingers would no longer stay curled around the bail. I tried two hands, with the pail in front of me, bobbing around with every step. This was no good whatever. Meanwhile I was plodding over the snowy road. I had three choices in walking. I could walk in the center at the risk of being run down by a car which would never see me for the falling snow, but this was slippery and a constant threat to the milk as well as to me. I could walk at the side, sinking down to my knees at every step. Or I could walk in the rut made by car wheels, but the rut was frozen and sharp and cut my ankle each time I slipped in it. I tried them all in turn, shifting the pail from one hand to another in the process. By the time I was halfway home the five quarts of milk weighed as much as a sack of cement. Every ten steps I was setting the pail down to rest. I no longer recovered between rests. My arms, fingers, and back ached, my shoulders felt as though they were permanently dislocated, I could hardly turn my head, my neck was so stiff. I thought of the cows back in the barn chewing their hay with that disgusting look of complacence. Dumb animals. Dumb, dumb animals, with no more sense than to give milk.

When I reached the kitchen door I literally had not the strength to walk up the steps and carry the pail inside. I sank down on the bottom step instead, breathed deeply, and rubbed my arms feebly with my hands. Probably this was an experience from which I should never recover. I was certainly maimed for life. And for what? For milk! Silly white cow juice that the men in my family drink morning, noon, and night. Good for making calcium in the bones—but calcium wouldn't help me now. I was long past calcium. I was even past bones. My arms were limp, turned to jelly.

When I was covered with snow, like the Babes in the Wood, and getting cold, I got up, gritted my teeth, grasped the milk pail with my final strength and both hands and carried it into the kitchen. It took me two cups of coffee and a half-hour by the stove to warm up and feel almost normal again.

It stopped snowing after lunch. "I ought to get the car out," the Professor said. "The battery will be dead. Guess I'll have to shovel out the barnyard."

I protested but he paid no heed. During the afternoon I could see him with his shovel, lifting huge mountains of snow and throwing them to one side. In an hour he had the drifts by the barn moved away so he could open the big double doors. Then he began on the driveway to the road. I wished the boys would come home and remembered they were going to a basketball game after school. Father would not get any help from them. But when I watched him from the north windows, he did not look tired; at least he was able to stand up and lift the shovel. And he was moving slowly toward the place where the barn driveway meets the road. He had driven the car out a few feet from the barn and left it with the engine going, white steam coming from the exhaust. By five o'clock, when it was nearly dark, he turned the lights on so he could see to shovel. Just before suppertime the boys came in, having walked up the hill.

"Did you stop and see your father?" I asked. "He ought to quit that shoveling. It's too hard for him."

The older boy said: "We wanted to help but he wouldn't let us. He's almost done. Said he'd be up in a few minutes."

"All right. Wash up. Dinner's about ready."

I heard the woodshed door open, and the Professor stamping the snow off his feet. "Just putting dinner on," I said to him. There was no answer. He was hanging up his coat and taking off his galoshes. When he stepped into the kitchen his face was very pale. He swallowed a couple of times as if he could not quite speak. Then: "I think I'm dying," he said slowly.

I ran to him but he put me aside. "I'll just go to bed," he said. "I don't want any supper. No, don't come with me, I can manage. You and the boys eat." Nevertheless, I went with him and saw him in bed, covered to the nose. He was almost instantly asleep. I went to look at him a couple of times before I went to bed myself, wondering if he really was ill and if I should call the doctor, but he was sleeping so soundly and so peacefully that I did not. I do not believe he moved for fourteen hours.

At supper the next night our younger son said: "Spring vacation next week—remember?"

I laughed. "Spring," I said. "Spring, indeed!"

"The calender says it is," the Professor remarked.

"What'll we do with the vacation?" This was from our older lad.

"I suppose we could build a snow fort," I suggested, with grim humor.

The Professor looked at all of us in turn. He seemed to be arriving at a momentous decision. But first he had to light a cigarette and pass his cup for more coffee. "When we are in town," he said at last, "we usually think of spending the spring vacation week up here in the country. This year, since we are here—" he hesitated and looked at us again—"how would you like to spend it in town?"

We had rented our house for the winter. "We haven't any place to stay in town," I said.

"There are hotels. We could get a couple of rooms and eat around at restaurants and go to the theaters—"

"And the movies—"

"And ride on the subway—"

"And no cooking or housekeeping—!"

"It will cost lots of money," our practical first-born said solemnly.

"And we've got it right in the bank," I assured him. For once it was true; we were a couple of hundred dollars ahead of schedule, ahead of taxes and mortgage payments and interest and income tax and the ever-present monthly bills.

"That settles it," said the Professor. "If the family financial expert says we can afford it, we'll go. How about Saturday morning?"

So we made our plans. My mother and a neighbor who could be called in for such an emergency were to stay in our house and keep the furnace going. The Professor arranged to see his publisher on business, which gave the trip a glimmer of necessity. The snowplow opened the road for us on Friday evening, but the wind was high and we decided it might not stay open until morning. So we packed our suitcases, fetched my mother and Esther to begin their residence at once, and drove the suitcases to the bottom of the hill where we left them and the car for our early departure.

Whatever the calendar said, it was dead winter when we walked down through the snowy road the next morning. Although we had our city clothes on, we still wore country footgear. But by the time we had gone twenty-five miles, the roads were clear and the snow was banked high on the sides. And incredible as it seems, at the outskirts of the city there was no snow at all, except now and then a little patch under a tree on the highways. Moreover, the sun had come out and we began to loosen wraps and think of warm weather.

No quartet of country bumpkins ever enjoyed the city more than we did. We went to the movies almost every afternoon and to the theater every night. We luxuriated in our warm, steam-heated rooms and fresh towels every day without the bother of washing them. We sampled every sort of place to eat from Chinatown to the Plaza. We slept late and took a nap before dinner and did not call up our friends, and I went shopping and the boys read comic books and in general we lived a completely irresponsible life for—not a week, but five days. On Thursday morning the Professor said: "I suppose everything is all right at home?"

"Dad wants some more winter," his older son said. "I don't mind. Let's go."

"It won't be winter even up there," I said. "I can't believe it." Which shows my ignorance. "But I'm ready, too."

So we had a last evening of a play and a taxi to the hotel and daily clean sheets and a hot bath. It had been fun. We had even enjoyed riding in the subway, which is strange, because although I like New York very much, I have never considered the subway particularly charming. It was the change, probably. It was no snow to shovel, no furnace to tend, no milk to fetch; for the boys, of course, it was no school. As we went up the West Side Highway, past the George Washington Bridge, I turned and looked back. It was a fine, bright morning, and the river and the big apartment buildings looked fresh and beautiful in the sunshine. But I was not sorry to be leaving, even though we must almost certainly expect more winter and more snow.

The two boys in the back seat grinned at me as I turned around. "Sorry?"

I shook my head. "Nice to be here, nice to go home," I answered. "I want to be there when the ice goes out of the pond."

22. *April Dressed in All His Trim*

WE like it when Easter comes after the middle of April. It means that the spring-vacation week in Connecticut coincides with spring itself; for except for a few freak early years when crocuses are pushing up at the end of March, our spring is typically New England, reticent, and late.

Years when we have spent the winter, it is different. Then we trace the first diffident swelling of winter buds, a slight activity in the forsythia branches, a fat spearhead of skunk cabbage, or galanthus thrusting up through the snow. The last full spring we spent in Connecticut we found that all the brilliant autumn colors are repeated, like ghosts of themselves, in spring. The youngest maple leaves are faintly pink, the catkins are faintly orange, the sassafras are on the way to purple, the willows are yellow, the dogwood stems are red, the hickories unbend smoky blue-green fingers. More nature-minded or even more observant country dwellers doubtless have known this all along, but the Professor and I, driving to the village one bright afternoon in March, saw it as a fresh and wonderful surprise.

April, even in ordinary years, does not bother with subtleties of faint uncurling leaf or inch-high spear of green. Knowing that it will be followed by May, April gets busy with early spring bulbs and hangs real flowers on them; with yellow forsythia branches; with a few apple buds that will open in the house if put in water; and having started the lilac leaves and pushed up the first grass, April can depart in a burst of daffodils.

After a winter in New York, a week of uncovering flowerbeds (even with considerable housecleaning thrown in as my portion) or planting early garden is a pleasure. Leaf-raking, a burden in October, becomes in April almost a joy. At least it doesn't last as long, there are not quite as many leaves, and they are wet enough to stick together in larger, if heavier, piles. Also there is the fun of finding things under them. I usually pull off the last layer of leaves gently with my hands. Even the most flexible bamboo rake breaks tender young shoots. The delphinium is about an inch high, pinky-green, serrated, not looking in the least as though it would mount to a six-foot blue spear. The phlox sends up a cluster of single shoots, prim and old-maidish looking. The oriental poppies present the same sawtooth green leaves they offered in the fall—so with the stone-crop, the chrysanthemums, the red rosettes of the primrose which at their blooming will be not red but butter-yellow. The tulips and hyacinths are coming along nicely, yellow where the leaf mulch has shut them from the sun, but they will green up in a couple of days. On the daffodils the buds are already fat. The crocuses are, of course, in bloom; nothing can daunt a crocus or a Johnny-jump-up. The Johnny-jumps are the Professor's favorite flower because they bloom regularly from March to December, and for all I know their small monkey faces go right on opening under the snow.

So we spend the spring week doing a little work—not too much—and admiring my garden (I say "we" and that is correct: I admire it without being urged; the men need only a little urging), planting peas and spinach and other indestructibles that probable later frost will not harm. We languidly pick up branches from the lawn, we look at the grass and say it will have to be cut next week maybe, we lie in the sun, we walk in the woods where there are still a few patches of snow, the Professor and at least one son play in the water. They clean out the intake to the pond, they pull piles of sopping-wet leaves out of the little brook that runs through my wild garden, they push ice cakes over the dam and watch them fall with a great boom and splash. The Professor does this because messing around in cold water is his passion; the boys do it for company, because they like to be with their father—perhaps because, by now, they have some idea of saving him the heavier kinds of work, although he doesn't seem to need such care.

Then it is Sunday—Easter Sunday—and in the evening we shall have to go back to New York for classes the next day. I remember particularly the last late Easter. We decided to go to church. I know that the faithful, who attend church regularly, look down on us shortsighted heathen who go on Easter Sunday. Why only once a year, they ask. If only once, why at all? I go at Christmas, too, I reply with dignity, but that does not seem to help. A holiday worshipper, they think me, and probably they are right.

Yet the Easter service, in Connecticut, when we are surrounded by our neighbors, is a very good and friendly thing. The church is the typical white weather-boarded building that the Congregationalists built all over New England. It is austere, decent, plain; there is no ornament outside and very little within. Flowers are banked at the front of the church—lilies and daffodils in pots with a background of hemlock branches—but there is not much music except the hymns sung by the congregation with the assistance of the choir—more neighbors. The church is crowded; we are not the only holiday attendants. The service is as plain as the building: a few hymns, a few baptisms, a handful of new members, announcements by the minister, a short sermon, and the benediction. There is no great organ pealing, no procession, no golden vessels, no acolytes in surplices. I do not mean that I object to the splendors of church ritual. If I were in New York and went to church I might very well go to the cathedral and be uplifted by the high pillars and the soaring music. Here, in the country, this unornamented meeting of friends on Easter Sunday seems to me right and happy.

We stopped after the service to greet a lot of people whom we had not seen since the fall before. We called on Jim and Helen, who instead of going to church were celebrating Easter by eating strawberries and cream in their sunny garden: the berries from their freezer, the cream from their own cow.

"How was church?" Jim asked. "Yes, we should have gone—should have. We thought about it . . . maybe next year—"

"You won't go next year, you know you won't," Helen said.

Jim ran his fingers through his hair. "Can't tell," he answered, his voice far away. "Can't tell what you'll do next year. Might go to church, yes. Helen's a minister's daughter, takes going to church kind of hard. Thing is to lean back and let it get you gently, if it does get you." We laughed and went away soon after that, I clutching a package of frozen strawberries for our dessert.

Jim is a New York writer who lives in our town all year, except for trips to the Algonquin or to Bermuda or Asheville now and again. I don't care whether he goes to church or not; I like to think of him sitting in his garden eating strawberries. That is a gesture to Easter Sunday, too—especially this kind of Easter Sunday.

When we get back to our house the thermometer by the side door says eighty in the sun. We shed our wraps and our Sunday clothes and take our sherry and Dubonnet out in the sun for a drink before lunch. The lunch is a ham that has been obligingly cooking away all by itself while we attended morning worship. In the angle of the kitchen and dining-room wings the crocuses and primulas are in riotous bloom; the flowers of the bleeding heart are already pink; the grass by the kitchen door is blue with violets that I shall have to dig up later on, but now I love them. Up in the garden the forsythia branches are sunny yellow. I think I have never seen a lovelier spring day than this and I say so, with nobody to contradict me.

"It smells so good," I say sniffing; then I look at the Professor and my sons. "At least it did smell so good a few minutes ago."

"You are now smelling young Herbert at an important spring duty," my younger son says dryly. I look in the meadow back of the house and there, sure enough, is the son of our farmer neighbor, mounted on a shiny green contraption, of all things a manure-spreader, spreading manure on Easter Day. The smell is quite strong by now, mixed as it is with new green leaves and young grass and upturned earth, but unmistakably the smell of the cowyard. Young Herbert, we learn presently, has been to church, has had his lunch, and is now doing the chore that needs to be done at the time available to him to do it.

We go in and tackle the ham and the strange smell follows us, not exactly unpleasant but undeniable. There is a big bowl of daffodils on the dining-room table—I picked them this morning. Daffodils smell particularly like spring, I always think, slightly astringent, not really sweet, but fresh, from the earth—from the newly awakening earth. The manure smell plays a double-bass accompaniment to the daffodil smell. We laugh about it and eat our ham and later Helen's strawberries with cream—from the bottle, not our own cow.

The spring day is not quite the same as it was this morning. Then it was sweet and clear; now it is mixed. But I cannot find it in my heart to wish that young Herbert had found another time to do his manure spreading. Tomorrow he must go back to high school. A farmer, which he is now and will be, must take advantage of the weather. This must be the perfect sort of weather to spread manure; ergo . . . the mixed smell on our lawn. It is probably only a convention anyway that a spring day should smell of new leaves and damp earth lately un-frozen, as much of a convention for some people as going to church regularly. There were those, I reflected, who would have been shocked at Jim and Helen happily eat-ing berries outdoors on Easter Sunday, or even at us four, who went to church but once or twice a year. We thought we were paying tribute to Easter and spring and our town and the friends we love; but we might have seemed dreadfully remiss to the old regulars. And far in the other direction, we have friends to whom the notion of going to church on any day never occurs.

Then there was young Herbert. He had made his de-votions, as with his parents he does quite regularly, and afterward he had put on his overalls and his big shoes and grabbed up a stalk of dried timothy to chew and he was ready for manure-spreading. I laughed when I thought how this would have been regarded by the old family who had come to our farm in 1775, shortly after the town was settled. I was sure that, if they had any religion at all—and I have no reason to think they did not—it was the austere, long-sermon, stiff-back, don't-work-on-the-Sab-bath kind. There are still farmers in our town who will not hay it on a Sunday be it never so sunny, be the threat of rain tomorrow never so strong, and the hay on the ground never so thick. Those few who, with good reason, do so are apologetic about it.

I was thinking of all this as I washed the dishes and

set them in the rack for the boys to dry for me. A couple of poet's narcissus stood in a glass on the shelf over the sink and I could lean forward over the dishpan and smell their deep sweetness. It took the manure smell temporarily out of my nostrils. For by now young Herbert was up near the house and going strong in more ways than one.

"That smell too much for you?" my older son asked. "Want me to shut the window?" The window was west, and fifty feet beyond it was Herbert with his burden. A fresh breeze that should have been laden with the scents of a warm spring day blew directly toward my nose.

"No, don't shut the window," I said. "Why should spring be just sweet smells? Spring is crocuses and it's manure, too. It's like everything—part reek and part Chanel No. 5." I wrung out the dishcloth and emptied the dishwater into the sink. The Professor came up behind me and stuck a daffodil over my ear.

"Quite the philosopher," he said. "Come outdoors. It's much too nice a day to spend in the house. I was coming to

help with the dishes, but since they're all done, I'll get out the chairs—unless you boys want to do it—and we'll relax."

Young Herbert was up in the orchard now and the breeze seemed to have died down. The boys spread a blanket and stretched out full length on it. The Professor put our two chairs side by side. I caught a distinct smell of bruised grass as I slid my chair around so it faced the sun. It was sweet, the sun was warm, we were all here together, and it was Easter Sunday in spring.

Date Due

Jan			
Oct. 6			
De 4 '52			
Ja 6 '53			
Demco 293-5			